Poetry IDOL

Treasured Verses

Edited By Byron Tobolik

First published in Great Britain in 2023 by:

Young Writers
Remus House
Coltsfoot Drive
Peterborough
PE2 9BF
Telephone: 01733 890066
Website: www.youngwriters.co.uk

Printed and bound in the UK by BookPrintingUK
Website: www.bookprintinguk.com
YB0550H

Foreword

Our latest competition, Poetry Idol, focuses on the people that these young poets look up to. This anthology is an impressive snapshot of the inventive, original and skilful writing of young people today, expressing their appreciation for the people, and things, that mean the most to them.

Here at Young Writers our aim is to encourage creativity in children and to inspire a love of the written word, so it's great to get such an amazing response, with some absolutely fantastic poems. It's important to focus on and celebrate others and this competition allowed these poets to write about who and what inspires them. The result is a collection of thoughtful and moving poems in a variety of poetic styles that also showcase their creativity and writing ability. Seeing their work in print will encourage them to keep writing as they grow and become our poets of tomorrow.

I'd like to congratulate all the young poets in this anthology, it's a wonderful achievement and I hope this inspires you to continue with your creative writing.

Contents

Gracie Chapman (13)	112	Isla Hobbs (9)	154
Zahra Ahmed (13)	113	Aizah Ramzan (11)	155
Beth Lamin (14)	114	Ellie Underwood (6)	156
Haadiyah Davis (9)	115	Ashley Watkinson (14)	157
Mustafa Mahmood (5)	116	Aminah Faisal (10)	158
Alec Bullett (17)	117	Harleen Hayer (12)	159
Laura Ann Houlder (12)	118	Brooke Hobbs (9)	160
Muhammed Khizar Khan (8)	119	Grayson O'Brien (7)	161
Naoise Dunne (10)	120	Maria Aitbaziz (14)	162
Elijah Conway (11)	121	Rose Greiff (12)	163
Lucy Andrew (9)	122	Ava Katiyo (9)	164
Samara Acton (11)	123	Imogen Buckle (12)	165
Billie-Marie Perry (11)	124	Daisy Langton (9)	166
Syed Muhammad Shahmir Hassan (11)	125	Lexie-Mai Collins (9)	167
		Sophie O'Sullivan (9)	168
Theodore Palmer-Clarke (3)	126	Jessica Stacey (11)	169
Uzma Sebagala (7)	127	Noor-Ul-Faatiha Mahmood (8)	170
Katie Yun Jue Hu (10)	128	Arabella Pasquariello (9)	171
Sofia Christophe (11)	129	Daisy Goldman (12)	172
Sofia Vallarino (8)	130	Poppy Raw (13)	173
Mimi Gross (16)	131	Riccardo Farinella (10)	174
Rose-Petal Needham (9)	132	Zhuxi Pan (8)	175
Chika Onukwuli	133	Nathan Robb (9)	176
Aaryan Madhav (9)	134	Olivia Grace (11)	177
Shreyashi Sinha (6)	135	Umme-Abiha Abid (9)	178
Allie Murray (14)	136	Zayden Cavanagh (9)	179
Kai Grainger (11)	137	Muhammad Faheel Saqib (10)	180
Cayla Bright (10)	138	Sophia Rood (8)	181
Dilyana Ivanova (10)	139	Manahil Ishaq (10)	182
Cattleya Fahmi (9)	140	Dominykas Krencius (11)	183
Elodie Douglas (10)	141	Mia Sturla (15)	184
Neferura Sukaina (9)	142	Brianna Chadwick (10)	185
Emelia Watts (11)	143	Mason Hicks (9)	186
Archsiga Jeyakumar (17)	144	Luna Clark (7)	187
Lylah White (11)	145	Melisa Ciparsone-White (10)	188
Noah Springthorpe (17)	146	Maisie Taylor (11)	189
Gracie-Leigh Bentley (12)	147	Alani Barmes (3)	190
Hana Gaspar (11)	148	Rita Santonastaso (6)	191
Ava McCracken (11)	149	Anya Elliott (13)	192
Zanna Eggertsen (9)	150	Darsh Desai (9)	193
Eliza Ball (9)	151	Lucia Grilli (13)	194
Rosie Oliver (15)	152	Aaroush Puniyani (7)	195
Daniel Murray (11)	153	Dexter Barrow (6)	196

Andrew Popa (8)	197
Vera Krauchuk-Muzhiv (10)	198
Imogen Rowson (8)	199
Henry Withnell (9)	200
Charlotte O'Brien (9)	201
Kairi Parry (10)	202
Aaron Aamir (6)	203
Myra Geldard (7)	204
Aisha Kausar (9)	205
Laaibah Ahmed (15)	206
Ava Giandiri-Davis (9)	207
Jessica Prestage (10)	208
Clara Farinella (7)	209
Max Hutton (13)	210
Libby Eggertsen (7)	211
Inaaya Imtiaz (10)	212
Alishba Kauser (12)	213
Adaah Afzal (14)	214
Shayla-Mai Irwin (11)	215
Holly Probin (11)	216
Aaron O-King (8)	217
Othniel-Levi Antwi (7)	218
Grace Coggins (9)	219
Poppy Teasdill (11)	220
Emile Krenciute (9)	221
Sophia Kate Russell (8)	222
Erin Daniels (8)	223
Mia Foster-Murray (5)	224
Princess (La'Lonia-Mai) Cooper (9)	225
Benjamin West (6)	226
Matias Cristea (6)	227
Amirah Osman (10)	228
Sophie Carberry (7)	229
Sasha Green (15)	230
Freya-Lilly Burrows (5)	231

The
Poems

My Dad

My dad works hard every day and night,
Salutes to the magpies who spread their wings and take flight!
My dad is special in every single way,
Making everyone around the world grin every day!
My dad is protective of Mom, Sofia and me,
He helped Sofia learn to ride a bike and me climb a tree!
My dad has many talents,
Chess and maths are just a few,
We all hope to be witty and inspiring like my dad too!
My dad is funny,
With his game, Daddy Land,
Letting us bury him in the golden sand!
My dad is the best,
It is hard to explain,
He is perfect,
The opposite of lame!
To Dad, on your special day,
I know joy and pride are heading your way.
Love Bella xx

Isabella Smith (9)

Adesua: My Favourite Person

Dedicated to Adesua Etomi-Wellington

Oh, Adesua, the actress of grace,
With a talent that lights up every space,
A beauty that captures all eyes,
And a spirit that soars up to the skies.

From her first role to her latest feat,
She's shown me what it takes to beat,
Against all odds, she strives for the best,
With passion and skill that never rests.

Through her craft, she's touched my heart,
With every line, she plays her part,
Bringing life to characters so true,
Making me feel like I knew.

She's a gem in the world of art,
With a humble heart, she's so pure and smart,
A wife, a mother and a friend,
Whose light will never come to an end.

Oh, Adesua, you inspire me,
To chase my dreams and to stand tall,

To embrace my flaws and own my might,
And to never give up on what's right.

May your journey be long and bright,
Filled with love, joy and delight,
And may you continue to shine,
Like a star that's always divine.

Ah, Adesua, the actress so fine,
Whose talent and beauty will always shine,
Though she doesn't know me, it's true,
My admiration for her will forever renew.

From afar, I've watched her career,
As she's climbed higher, year by year,
With every role she takes on the stage,
She brings to life characters of every age.

She's a source of inspiration, for sure,
A beacon of hope that will always endure,
Though we've never met, and may never do,
My admiration for her will always be true.

For she's shown me what it takes,
To follow my dreams, to make no mistakes,
To strive for excellence no matter the cost
And to believe, in what I have lost.

So, here's to you, Adesua, the star,
Who shines so bright no matter how far,

You may be far from me but in my heart,
You'll always have a special part.

Ah, Adesua, the actress so strong,
Whose journey has been tough and long,
Through trials and challenges, she's persevered,
And emerged stronger, with nothing to be feared.

She's faced the world with grace and poise,
Even when met with the toughest noise,
Her spirit never wavers, always true,
A shining example of what I should pursue.

From her past struggles, she's gained much insight,
And uses it to fight for what's right,
To uplift those who may be down,
And bring light to those who may wear a frown.

Through it all, she's never lost hope,
And inspires me to find my own rope,
To climb out of the darkness and despair,
And find the light that's waiting there.

So, here's to you, Adesua, the fighter,
Whose strength and resilience inspire,
You've shown me what it truly means,
To face adversity and make it a scene.

May you continue to shine and soar,
And inspire others to do even more,

For you're a beacon of hope and might,
A star that will forever burn bright.

Favour Abimifoluwa Ishola (15)

Cadence

When I was a child, my heart drummed with the cadence of
her footsteps,
My stocky form moved with the grace of her shadow.
My tongue sought the sophistication of hers;
Mirrored the clicks and tuts and lilt of hers,

Because even then, she was my muse;
Guiding my hands as they worked the loose clay of my
words,
Smiling, nudging me on.

It was my muse who taught me laughter,
Who taught me to burst so earnestly and boisterously that
It was only her I allowed to hear it:
The song of my happiness.

It was my muse who taught me sorrow,
Who taught me to let my tears flow freely despite heckling
juvenile voices calling, "Crybaby."
She taught me that my tears and my sobs were the first
evidence that I was alive,
They set me apart from a dead man - rigid and frigid.

It was my muse who taught me grief:
bitter, gut-wrenching grief.
Who taught me what it felt like for a piece of your heart to
be given to another,

And have them plucked away, your fragmented soul
clutched ever so tightly in their desperate hands.

It was my muse who taught me life,
Who taught me how to thrum with a rhythm of my own;
Du-dum, du-du-dum...
She taught me how to know my truth and how to spew it,
Unflinchingly, unapologetically,
Even though the world has never been so kind as to lend the
black woman the mic.

Muse taught me love;
The heat that blankets your soul when cradled to the chest
of a beloved,
The extraordinary state of being a beggar and an addict all
at once;
Opening your heart up to a person,
Investing in them an invaluable fragment of your heart,
all for that feeling,

That heat...

The Norse have a word for it - *peiskos*.

This is a love letter to my muse;
A thank you to end all thank yous...
Every minute of every day,
Every time I look at you, a rhythm pulses in my mind,
I love you, I love you, I love you;
I want to yell it at the top of my lungs in every tongue
known to man,

Because it is true. And every time those words fall from my lips,
They beat with the cadence of my heart because if there truly is a life after this,
I'll love you then too.

Because you gave me a gift above all else -
A gift you continue to give:
Yourself. Your youth. Your nurturing...

Motherhood.

It was my muse who taught me to stand proud,
Who taught me that one's countenance could very well be the key to many doors,
Who taught me that treating my body like the temple that it is made me feel like one,
Built on gold to house gold and nothing less.

Because of Muse, my heart beats with a cadence of my own
And my words are an arrow flying free;
singing my truth to the tune of the wind,

Hitting the world where it hurts.

Winifred Otubo (14)

Marilyn Monroe

The American actress, so famous and bold,
And her personality shone like gold.
Born in 1926, in June,
Her acting was as bright as the moon.
Her head was held high,
Right up to the sky.
Feeling brave and proud,
Making her voice outstanding and loud.
When she set foot on the stage,
Everybody stared at her in a daze.
Her iconic dress,
Was made sure to impress.
The movement must catch the audience,
It was guaranteed to be an astonishing performance.
Then things came to a turn,
As her mental health began to burn.
She thought she would be happy taking drugs,
But she needed more than a supply of hugs.
Darkness came straight at her,
As her life was whisked away into a blur.
She was always remembered as she passed away,
But this was the quote, this was her last say,
"Say goodbye to Pat. Say goodbye to Jack (President Kennedy). And say goodbye
To yourself, because you're a nice guy." - Marilyn Monroe.

Tilly Burridge (12)

Oh Fiction

Oh fiction, every time you greet me, I escape
I can mend the wound created by the pain of reality before it's all too late
The pages flicker in my grasp, the pretty words linger in my mind as if I have bought dopamine for free
Each character comforts me, each conversation I think about, am I too blind to see reality?

Oh fiction, I enjoy feeling powerful and loved
As all the characters laugh and save the world, their experiences become mine, I become beloved
I imagine their pain, their trauma, their sobbing eyes and they bring a waterfall into mine
But what I can never seem to understand, is my own story, reality is not correctly designed

Oh fiction, reality has empty words taking you to bottomless depths, some pages are blank, and some are ripped apart whilst others are written in the richest of inks
The world of fiction is huge with sweet danger, but each day, this reality shrinks
How I wish I could spend every moment inside of fiction
Where just out of reach are all my predictions

Oh fiction, you are a thing of wonder
But reality grabs me by the wrist and drags me away, I must surrender

You excite me and all I want is to open the door of phenomenon and allow the words to dissolve in this magical view
Why is it that you cannot take me with you?

Oh fiction, don't leave me here, where burdens bring you down and people leave.
Fiction, I beg of you to not leave me in this isolated world where we must grieve.
With your hand in mine, fiction, I can grow, win wars, rule kingdoms and salvage the world thousands of times.
But each time the pages end, you leave me behind in this world, where I simply stare at the wall and think of rhymes.

Oh fiction, I will never forget what you have given
I have adored each moment with you but now the time is up, you are forgiven
Tomorrow, I will pick up another book and flutter the pages in my grasp
And hope to feel at home, as I put the book down, the thought knocks on the door and I gasp
Oh fiction, you are my shield
But if it's fiction, then why does it feel so real?
In this imaginary world, none of it was ever existent,
Nonetheless, in my mind, the words, characters and passion dance
I want to sink in the magic of literature and wipe the tears of poetry, please come back and give me a chance...
Oh fiction, oh fiction, oh fiction.

Mishel Rafiq (13)

Idol?

I never had an 'idol' as a child.
I may have admired Jerry for his courage against Tom,
I may have respected Henry for his famous stink bomb.
And although as a child I watched every movie,
Not once did I think, *that is who I want to be.*

'Cause what is an 'idol' anyway?
Someone you want to imitate? You think highly of?
Someone who shows you a special kind of love?
Someone who raises and never gives up on you?
Or someone who turns you into someone new?

I never had an 'idol' as a young girl.
Greta Thunberg changed the world, protested and objected,
Emma Watson changed my heart, spoke and connected.
Their courage and strength I once again admired,
Yet were they the 'idols' who I so desperately desired?

But what is an 'idol' anyway?
Do I want to be like them? Do they inspire me?
Are they who I will look up to, who I want to be?
People I have never met, who I know only from the news?
Or do I need to know them, someone who I never lose?

I never had an 'idol' growing up.
My dad is a hard worker giving us so many successes,
My mum is so generous and her big heart still progresses.

Their sacrifices and life struggles are hard to comprehend,
But are they who will put my search to an end?

So tell me, what is an 'idol' anyway?
Someone who puts the family's needs before their own?
Or someone who I know I can always call my home?
Though they are the people who make me feel safe,
Why aren't they the role models I so desperately crave?

I finally found my idol as a teenager.
Someone who struggles to get through every day, yet never gives in,
Someone who's made so many mistakes, yet has fixed their every sin.
They struggle in silence, their pain never noticed,
No one ever there to hug when they're at their lowest.
For they're the person I once aspired to be,
The resilience and strength which I needed in me.

For I am now my own idol.
A person I now respect.
A person I now accept.
Proud of what I am, who I've become.
Proud of my final outcome.
I am my own idol.

Habiba Hassan (17)

Who I Admire

She's the strongest woman I know
And the most beautiful woman I've ever seen
She may not think she's strong or beautiful though
But to me, she's the most stunning human being.

She's full of honesty
She's the toughest,
And most importantly,
She's the realest
And has the most kindness.

She's fought so many battles
And yet still has the biggest heart
She's like candles,
Constantly relighting after being blown out.

She doesn't give up either,
She's so determined to keep going
No matter what's happening near her or to her
She's always glowing,
Like a little star
Nothing's stopping her from shining.

I admire her so much because
She does her best for me
She honestly deserves a round of applause
Since there's no guarantee that I'm easy.

Her smile is genuine,
And her eyes are full of happiness,
All big and glistening,
While she looks at the people she loves.

Her hand holds mine
Whilst she leads me in the right direction.
As long as she's with me, everything's fine.

And within what she calls her 'imperfections',
I see a woman who's doing her best,
Doing the most
And trying her hardest
For her family and what she calls home.

She has a heart of gold,
Always doing what's best
However old
She gets, I'll always be blessed
To have someone in my life like her.

She continuously encourages me to be my best self,
And she never stops trying her hardest
I'd love to have the same resilience as herself,
Despite how hard life can get

She's raised me well
And taught me so much
You know, sometimes people tell

You that there's no such
Thing as a perfect person.

But I'm definitely certain
That my mum's one
Of the perfect people.

Kiera Crouch (14)

The Definition Of A Mother

What is a mother? A question you could discover in life,
A person that would guide you through the strain and the strife.
A mother is someone like no other,
She can be known as the strongest lover.

Her face is welcoming as her heart is merciful,
Looking into her tender eyes can make you feel purposeful.
Galaxies and wonders can be waiting in her mind,
But she would only open it up to a trusting person that she would find.

I would always give your personality my greatest admiration,
Because your personality is always famous for its fascination.
You have always encouraged me with the dreams I want to achieve,
And your amiable words make me think my dreams are right there for me to retrieve.

Even when you have passed on and you're an angel to be,
I know you will always be there right beside me.
Because you are a legend; it is known low and high,
And the truth is that legends never die!

Emily Overton-Braesyde (11)

To My Number One

Today, I got an email,
Asking me to write a poem,
A poem about my favourite person,
My all-time number one.

I debated between my two best friends,
Amelia and Kateryna,
But then I realised,
It wasn't either of them,
I love them to pieces, don't get me wrong.
But the person who held the title,
The title of my favourite person,
Was sat by my side.

She's the one that's been there always,
The one who has my back when I am depleted,
The one who sat there and waited,
While I had that operation.

The one whose shoulder I cry on,
The one I trust with my life,
The one who annoys me every day,
But I'm sure I do the same to her,
The incredible woman who gave me life.

My mum.
She's been there since day one,

And she's never not been there,
But I give her hardly any credit.

I don't thank her every day,
Even after all she's done for me,
The amazing things she does for me,
The measures she goes to.

There's this saying I adore,
To the world, you're just a mum,
To me, you are the world,
I love it,
It's completely accurate for me,
But I don't tell her nearly as much as I should.

My mum is Super Mum,
She can do anything,
I'm so proud of her,
I'm proud to call her my mum,
The business she has created,
The life she has forged.

The money she has spent,
To give me the life I have,
A life where I can follow my dreams,
Just like I'm doing now,
Writing these poems,
Writing these books,

It's all thanks to her,
For encouraging and helping me.

So, to my favourite person,
Thank you for being there,
Thank you for loving me,
Thank you for everything,
Because I love you,
And I'm sorry I don't tell you that every day.
Thank you, Mum.

Grace McCullough (12)

My Mom

For my idol, I chose my mom.
I love my mom more than words can express.

She sacrifices her time and life to make sure she's always there for me.
She has set the standards and paved the way for what a hardworking, independent, strong woman looks like.

I believe having your mother as your idol is a beautiful thing,
A testament in itself to how well she has raised me.
Every daughter says her idol is her mother,
But I look at my mother and realise how much I look up to her and never want to let her down,
She has provided for me tirelessly and has always attended every school play, parents' evening, dance show, appointment etc.

She's worked overtime and had sleepless nights,
To make sure I get the things I wanted,
And she has never *ever* failed me once.

She is my mom, my superhero and best friend all in one.
Mom, I love you to the moon and back.

Kareena Thumber (15)

Stay

Are you and her still friends?
I hope so, 'cause I don't want it to end,
Maybe it has ended and I don't know it yet
Or maybe it hasn't and this is all a dream
And I just miss who we used to be
Maybe this is a fever dream
Maybe it's the only way I'll know
But in all honesty, I don't know
In all honesty, I don't know how honest I am
Writing all these poems while thinking about someone that
acts all glam
In all honesty, every word that rhymes
Is another sentence,
Another poem,
Of divine
And I miss the way we were
The songs we played
And the things we swore
I miss the way you smiled
The way you never cursed
And when you did,
It was probably the funniest thing on Earth.
I miss it every goddamn day
And I am only here to say
Here to stay,

I am here
Far and near
I am here
Forever and always
No matter what they say
Every single day
Even if you won't talk to me
Even if you won't come with me
Even if you won't be here for me
Just know
That no matter which way we go
I will always go
The way that suits you best
Because, my friend, you are all in my head
So when they say,
"Are you still friends?"
Well, I say,
I don't know
I hope so
I don't know so
I only hope so
Which is the only thing I do
I hope away in my little heart
Until I find something
Another way,
Another way to remain friends with you,
Another way to say,

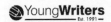

Stay.
Stay with me
Even if I have to fall to my knees
Stay.
Stay for time
Stay for life
Stay until I go
Until I leave
And I will do so equally.
So when they ask,
"Are you still friends?"
Tell me,
Are we?
Or has it come to an end?
Is this all in my head
Or must I find another friend instead?

Evie Goode (13)

Lonely Life Of Lies

The spring sprung by
As the summer melted past
The autumn waltzed through.
However, the winter lingered and didn't move on
With an endless ringing of the knell

The sun glimpsed past the greyness of our lives
Rain poured in oxygen
And the abysmal wind cleared the obstacles for life.
But the cold, icy clouds just don't sweep past.

There yonder the ice-hidden window,
A lighthouse scattered desperately
To find a small rocking boat in peril with the stormy, chilly
sea.
Like an abandoned bee,
Struggling to fly out of its own honey.

Suddenly, the endless icy music ceased,
A spotlight shone to help the mole claw its way to the
surface.
Just as all hope was lost,
Birds spoke of their arrival,
As trees blossomed with optimism.

Fruits only appear when the tree is ready.

Harijeeth Reddy Parvatha (14)

The Beautiful Game

The tunnel leaked with white shirts,
With players grateful and proud.
They gritted their teeth, eyes a-twinkle,
As they roared the anthem loud.

With the slice of a neon boot,
The Euro Final had begun.
England would pass, dribble, tackle, shoot,
'Til, against Germany, they'd won.

The team was the best England had ever seen:
An agile goalie with a solid defence,
Tekky and pacey mids and subs,
Paired with a striker who won't give the opposition a
chance.

Though their game is toned to perfection,
It is their mentality that sets these players apart,
Determination, passion and resilience,
Barricading prejudice from flooding their hearts.

As the winning goal raced into the net,
The hard work of this team was revealed,
And the piercing whistle ploughed joy into their brains,
Whilst to the drenching triumph, they kneeled.

This victory banished years of hurt and yearning,
But not for reasons you might have expected;
See, this team was not the Lions, but the Lionesses,
And it took this glory for girls' footie to finally be accepted!

Not just these women had to face discrimination,
Instead, all the females in the beautiful game,
But because they were honest, pure and proud,
They knew that football is for *everyone*, not just males.

The tangled tale of women's football: perseverance, skill and determination,
Will be forever etched into the stars,
For these talented players paved the way, blazed a trail,
And it is their path I want to walk, their legacy I want to build my future upon to show this beautiful game is all of ours.

Evelyn Bussey (11)

My Mother

Belinda, my mother, so strong and kind,
Her love and guidance, always on my mind.
Her heart so full, her spirit bright,
A mother's love, a guiding light.

With open arms, she welcomes all,
Her love is unconditional, it never falls.
Her words of wisdom, her gentle touch,
A mother's love, it means so much.

Through all life's ups and downs we've been,
Her love and support, a constant theme.
Her unwavering faith, her endless care,
A mother's love, beyond compare.

Belinda, my mother, my guiding star,
In my heart, you'll always be not far.
A mother's love, forever true,
I'll always be grateful for you.

Belinda, her name so sweet,
A mother's love, so pure and complete.
Her heart so gentle, her spirit kind,
A mother's love, a treasure to find.

With arms so warm and a smile so bright,
She's there to guide you through the night,

Her words of wisdom, her endless care,
A mother's love, beyond compare.

She's there to wipe away your tears,
To calm your fears and ease your fears,
Her love so strong, her spirit bright,
A mother's love, a shining light.

Belinda, a mother so true,
Her love so pure, her heart so new,
A mother's love, forever strong,
A gift of love to cherish lifelong.

Isabelle Denning (13)

The Mummy Of My Dreams

She loved and cared for me before I was born,
She never let me rip or tear,
She was the first one to touch my skin,
Before it all begins.
I didn't know how fierce I could be,
Until it came to protecting you.
You soothe me with your kindness,
that travels for miles.
You're the sunshine to a dark day,
We'll never let the wind blow our friendship away.
To describe how much I love,
The woman I call Mummy.
As dusk ends the day,
She blows the dust away.
Mum, the way you hold my hand,
The way you care for me,
You taught me bravery,
With your velvety tenderness.
The way you look after me,
You teach me and guide me.
Kindness is the colour of pink,
It smells like candy floss.

My mum, the one I look up to,
To love me so I can show my love.
Bestest of friends forever and always,
She has the most beautiful smile,
She sounds like a waterfall,
She feels like a soft, fluffy blanket.
Just a little kindness can go a long, long way,
Mum, without you there would be no home.
She looks like a blooming flower,
That I would pick every day,
She tastes like a cold lolly,
On a hot summer's day.
She is not just my mum,
She is my friend,
My mum made me the person I am today,
I'm forever grateful.

Scarlett-Grace Webb (10)

Unworshipable Idol

Emmy, Grammy, Oscar and Tony Awards,
I bet no knight can win all these, even if they fight with swords,
Some people die just to meet these idols,
But I would rather kill them with kindness,
Like Selena Gomez.
Zendaya, Jennifer Lawrence and Emma Watson all think they're perfect girls,
But, I mean, they aren't as pretty as pearls,
I admit, I am jealous, so I just 'Shake It Off',
Isn't that right, Taylor Swift?
When people idealise these actors and singers,
I want to blow up like a grenade because they aren't always winners,
And besides, they're ageing, so they can't remain successful beginners,
I do not have the heart to worship them because my heart is in Havana.
I can be just as good a singer as Harry Styles, Adele and even Justin Bieber,
Because 'There's Nothing Holding Me Back',
And also, because it's my 'Last Christmas' so...
Wham!
Tom Cruise, Tom Holland or Helena Bonham Carter,
They're all worth millions of dollars,
So when they waltz away with shiny awards, it feels like torture.

I won't be rude,
But I love the dresses that are worn by these unworshipable
idols, they leave me bejewelled
These idols will always be unworshipable,
Because they have done hard work to be what they are,
And so can we
So get off of your sofa or I'll have to do it myself with a
crowbar!

Zoya Hasan (12)

The Girl Who Led An Army

She fought against injustice,
She fought for liberty,
She fought despite many around her being in poverty.
She sailed to other countries,
She finished her work over many centuries.
She awakened people with her words,
She never let a single follower be unheard.
She witnessed many of her followers get murdered,
It broke her heart but didn't stop her fight,
She just knew it had to be made right.
Tyranny and wrongdoings plague everywhere,
But she helped to reduce sexism over here.

The current uprising of women in Iran,
Where they're demanding their civil rights,
Is where I like to be their voice,
To shout, their courage, their chants, not just a noise.
While people in other countries just watch and rejoice,
It is their choice to assist,
But still, they choose to resist.
For the girls and women of Iran,
Their fight and determination goes on,
They fight and fight until the break of dawn.
For me, a girl pampered in comfort in every way,
The mission is to encourage the world to say their name.

I will always look up to her from the past,
She was a female activist, but not the last.
She made it her mission to help women,
My mission is to do the same,
Making sure women aren't property to claim,
Making sure there is no villainy,
Like women in Iran, opposing tyranny.
She was Emeline Pankhurst.

Mahpary Ghorbany (11)

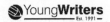
My Little Sister, Aria

I always wanted a sister or a brother
So I continuously begged my mother
What I got wasn't a brother
But a baby sister, Aria - I love her
We're always there for one another
Thinking of her in pain, I shudder
It's fun seeing things she discovers
She's my little sister, Aria - I love her
When Dad's trying to eat supper
Or when Mom's having a cuppa
I will try very hard to cover
Just because I love her...
That even though I'm tougher
When we play fights, she's rougher
But I will never shove her
Because I really truly love her
I pretend that I'm her mother
For that, I am a bluffer
I don't need a brother
I have Aria - I love her
When she hurts herself, she blubbers
So where she's hurt, I rub her
For I don't want her to suffer
She's my sister and I love her
Though times we annoy each other

I'll always kiss and hug her
For a friend, I need no other
I have Aria - I love her
Although sometimes she's a bother
I thank God, my father and mother
For giving me a sister, not a brother
Named Aria - I'll always love her.

Athena Christopher (9)

Mr Cannon

I'll soon be leaving primary school,
So I've written this little verse,
About Mr Cannon who's really cool -
Probably the best teacher on Earth!*

Mr Cannon always helps in a tricky situation,
When we're stuck on things we don't know,
He's taught us fractions and long multiplication,
He has really helped us to grow.

When it comes to accents, Mr Cannon is king,
He makes us giggle every day,
His magic tricks are ace and he's very daring,
I love the pranks that he plays.

Mr Cannon tells us lots of great tales,
But we are always wanting more,
Like when he got so much Valentine's mail,
He couldn't get through the door!

When it came to the Year Six show,
Mr Cannon got a bit stressed,
So many dances and lines to know,
We put his patience to the test.

I'll always remember 'Feel Good Fridays',
And singing songs on the coach from Stackpole,

Strictly Come Dancing and the Clap Game -
Year Six was so rock 'n' roll!

With a wink and a fist bump, we'll soon say goodbye,
I'm sad it's the end of the beginning,
But I'll always remember these happy times,
And when I look back, I know I'll be grinning!

*Along with Mrs Cannon, who is also really wonderful!

Faith Lydall (11)

My Idol

People say there's only one
In my mind, there are five
But if I'm being honest
This one never leaves my mind
She helps me
I help her
She works her hardest every day
And turns my frown upside-down
She takes charge
She speaks her mind
She keeps her composure
When they're not being kind
I trust her with everything
And she will do the same
We share our clothes and make-up
All our shoes and toys
Nothing is just mine or hers
It's ours and ours alone
We will be together
Never live apart
Nothing can pull us apart
Even through death, we'll be one
And share our favourite plans
It's me and her against the world
We are a two for one

My friends are hers
Her friends are mine
We share and share alike
To me, she is special
To me, she is kind
To me, she is the most amazing
Thing on Earth itself
I love her
She loves me
She's known me all my life
She chose my name
And made me smile
My sister
All my life.

Ellie Louise Bunce (14)

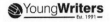

I Rise

You may torment and abuse me,
You make me cry, but why do you never apologise?
You might smother giggles at me and torture me,
But I'm like a balloon with helium inside it, I rise.

Just like stars shimmering and shining at twilight,
Should I terrifically be petrified?
I'm on a mission to be more resilient,
Still, I rise.

Is it possible you dearly want to see me drenched in my own tears?
Do you want to see my swollen, bloodshot eyes?
Do you want to engulf my life in sadness?
Why tell lies?

On the ocean's surface, swimming in the open sea,
I rise,
Swimming freely, I'll unlock my happiness with my key,
I rise,
I'm Poseidon, protecting the oceans,
I'm a good witch with my happiness potions,
I rise.

Escaping long, long years of shame and pain,
Into a beautiful horizon that blossoms me into a new person,

I will fight for what I think is right,
I will be everything for the light,
I rise,
I rise,
I rise.

Rhea Verma (10)

My Hero

When I am lonely,
I search for you in my heart.
I find you in the memories,
All the special moments we shared from the start.

No one can beat you,
You are my one and only.
Sadly, you left me,
Since then, I have never felt so lonely.

To this day, nothing has changed,
Nothing has been forgotten.
When I close my eyes, I see us
In every moment, we are always together.
No one else will ever be better.

I will never lose your values, character and kindness,
Your smile was always a likeness.
The lessons you taught me will stay with me forever,
You were so inquisitive and clever.

I loved hearing about how you used to hide
The sweets away from my sneaky mother,
She tried to find a way but you always found her!

You will always be my hero,
My beloved grandad (Nanu),
You are the greatest blessing that I have ever had.

You will forever be with me,
Guiding me through my fears
And helping me accomplish my career!

Zunairah-Emaan Imran (11)

What's My Barbie Role?

What is my Barbie role?
Am I the girl with blonde hair and blue eyes?
Am I the girl that shines above all the other dolls?

No, I'm not.

I'm the Raquel, the one with black hair and dark eyes.
The one portrayed as the villain in every tale you tell.
The one who stands on her own without a Ken to put under her spell.

I'm the Raquel.
I'm the one pushed down in the world full of Barbies.
I'm the one you tell to sit tight and be polite while others tell their story.

What about mine?
What about my story?
Does my vision really blind Barbie's glory?
And why should I have to hide?
To keep my head down and myself to myself.
Why?

Because of my skin?
Is it really a sin?

Am I a sin for being who I am?
Or am I a controversial topic?

Why should I scrub off my skin,
Just to fit in?
Is it because I'm not the Barbie?

Well, I'm not the Barbie.
And I don't want to be, for I am the Raquel,
Black hair, dark eyes and skin as soft as the night.

I don't want your glory
You can have it all.
Because being the Barbie is not my role.

Massara Alazzawi (15)

Legend Of A Lakshmi Bai - The Rani Of Jhansi

This is a story of a Rani of strength,
A true warrior in every sense,
She was the bravest queen,
With care in her eyes, she looked serene.

In the land of India, long ago,
When an extraordinary thing happened,
Fearless, brave, Lakshmi Bai,
Fought with her might till the end.

She led her troops into the battle,
Determined for freedom, never did she rattle,
Her sword of justice was always raised high,
In courageous acts, open to defy.

It took her four places to go to
And build her army strong,
She taught them fighting skills
And how to stay all along.

A true legend for people to know,
A shining star that will always glow,
Who fought for freedom till the endless light,
A fearless soul shining bright, fighting for her people day
and night.

The Rani of Jhansi was kind and caring,
Her brave acts were bold and daring,
Her perseverance was a symbol of victory,
A royal fighter who shall always live in history.

Aryahi Tewari (10)

To My Sister

I was drawn to you from the moment my eyes met yours
I knew we'd be inseparable
And indeed, we were
We always had each other's back
The world is a much better place with you.
Even though you grew up
We were still the best of friends
All the times we fought and argued.
I knew it was our way of showing love
We could never go more than three days without talking to each other
You were and still are my everything
I know you think I am strong and I am
But the thought of us being separated makes me weak
You were like the mother my heart craved
But I would never admit it to you
I don't know why God made you my sister
But I'm glad he did
Because a world without you is not a world for me
I want to hurt those who hurt you
Turn your tears into joy
But I can't do anything yet
I want you to know I'm proud of you
I can't wait for us to start a new chapter in our lives
Away from the people who hurt us

You are stronger than you think.
You are smarter than you think
And I will always be by your side to remind you of this.

Lawrensa Addea (17)

To My Hero: Me, Myself And I

I have a lot to be thankful for,
Even though sometimes I wish I had more,
But if there's one thing that's enough for me,
It's the never-ending confidence in my body,
So thank you me, myself and I.

Sometimes when I feel like I'm losing,
When I feel like I can't keep moving,
And my thoughts seem to betray me,
My conscience never ceases to amaze me,
And I can never thank myself enough,
Thank you me, myself and I.

There are times when I feel like I'm drowning,
And I wish I could stop sinking,
And so the confidence starts to decay,
But my mind always manages to keep it at bay,
And I can never thank myself enough,
Thank you me, myself and I.

So when you feel the doubt creeping up on you,
Don't let it grow into something new,
Don't ever let it grow or prosper,
So make sure to remember,

To always thank yourself enough,
And to always say, "Thank you me, myself and I."

Chimamanda Onyekonwu (12)

As The Sun Goes Down

For my mum on Mother's Day

As the sun goes down
on Hampton town

The mums are working hard
They chop and cut the food we eat
And write our birthday cards...

As the sun goes down on
Hampton town

Flu has come
And so has Mum
With her antidote

As the sun goes down on
Hampton town

The mums give us joy
Holidays, TV and
They give us Pokémon like Eevee
And organise our stuff

As the sun goes down on
Hampton town

I drive her crazy
And can be lazy
And refuse to go to bed

As the sun goes down on
Hampton town

She buys me sushi
And a dessert that is mushy
But I like it all the same

As the sun goes down on
Hampton town

I make comments that are witty and wise
And Mum watches me with her big eyes

She tells me to sleep, eat and wake up
She puts on her lipstick and her favourite make-up

As the sun goes down on
Hampton town

Sometimes I make her coffee
While she buys me toffee

She cares for me a lot
The love and worry
The friendship and duty
Is all that really matters

As the sun goes down on
Hampton town

And the amazing bond goes on...

Arjun Dudhe (10)

Be Like Him

Although my role model is from the past,
I remember him often, his teachings keep me steadfast,
He holds a special place in many hearts,
But in his life, he was seen by his family as an outcast,
And the way he responded to the hostility will leave you aghast,
For even today, his life lessons spread vast.

Never in a breath did he utter a lie,
His words were soft, his actions kind,
He adored his daughters, sadly his sons never survived,
He was an orphan and an incredible husband, a gem to his wife,
And would give charity to the poor, he advised all the time,
For he was respectful to everyone and was humble all his life.

Who is this man? I hear you ask,
Go and study his life, that is your task.

He's the best of mankind and has the purest of hearts...
Breathe like him, feel like him, see like him, be like him!
He is my prophet and is the last.

Humayra Shafi (12)

The Touch Of The Spirit

My dearest father,
Fly so high.
The stars will shine,
Glimmer and rise,
Seeing now as you have tried.

Take my hand,
Hold it tight.
Grasp my touch
And keep in sight.
Reach my calls
Until it's light.
Never to leave,
Never to cry.

Not a second goes by
Where I don't feel fright,
Thinking now
I've lost my fight
Safe you are,
In my heart,
There shall stay
Most by far.

Heaven you go,
So peacefully.

Ribbons may flow
Above the sea.

At times, I may smile,
Laugh and teach
But at times, I stumble,
Fall and weep.
There are times
I feel so weak,
Caused by the pain
Of the grief.

Now I see so gracefully,
An angel looking
Down at me,
Make me proud
Make me smile,
Make me go the extra mile.
Let me show you
The eyes of me,
Only then you will see
How wild life can really be.

Lucky paths,
Some at least
May not be the best we see,
Lead the way
Guide the peace,

There you rest
In the presence of me.

Tanisha Logan (13)

Follow Me

Looking in the mirror in the morning
I heard a voice in my head calling
"This is your future and your own idol
This is your everything and who you are."
I thought 'bout it until I began to understand
I guess it's time for me to take a stand
Letting others rule and control my life
It needs to be stopped because my life is mine!
I show the world what's inside me
If I don't, who's going to do it for me
I hate the word 'me' to show another guy
I guess it's their job, I don't think it's mine
Lead me, guide me through this maze
Show me what is the correct way
Don't force me, rule me in this game
If you can't, then let me, myself, play
I am as timid as a rabbit when I play
Don't make me a lion, stand in my way
If life is a game, victory is my name
Young children, kids, I'll be an idol for them.

Methsari Bihansa (16)

A Girl Who Had Hope

A girl who had hope
Humongous hope,
She is grateful,
Like a wave of inspiration,
Her diary is blessed, and she is brave,
She's Anne Frank.

A place of petrifying death,
Behind a bookcase, there is deafening silence,
A girl writing in her diary,
About how everyone had good in them,
She's Anne Frank.

She is Jewish,
Scared,
But strong and hopeful,
Writes about the horrors of war,
So moving,
So inspiring,
She is Anne Frank.

Eventually, they found her,
She died in a concentration camp,
Life was ghastly,
Life had terrible conditions,
She died from disease,

Her father - the only one to survive,
He published her book.

She is famous now,
She had the hope of a trillion men,
She was an inspiration,
A light in the dark,
Was honest and great,
Was ambitious,
She's Anne Frank.

Loyal,
Optimistic,
Brave,
Powerful,
Strong,
Loving,
Patient,
Had a beautiful diary,
It is blessed,
It is sad,
But admired,
Always remember,
Always have hope,
And always keep on dreaming,
She's Anne Frank.

Sarah Ward (10)

A Mother's Love

A mother's love is like no other,
A bond that lasts forevermore,
Her heart beats for her child's safety,
Her love, a never-ending story.

She carries her child for nine long months,
And then she brings them into the light,
From that moment on, she'll do all she can,
To keep them safe both day and night.

She'll kiss away the tears they cry,
And hold them close when they feel scared,
She'll be their rock when times are tough,
And show them how much she has cared.

She'll teach them how to walk and talk,
And guide them through life's ups and downs,
She'll be their friend, their confidante,
And help them chase away their frowns.

A mother's love is unconditional,
It knows no bounds or limits set,
It's a love that lasts a lifetime long,
And one that we should not forget.

So here's to all the mothers out there,
Who give their all each and every day,

You are the ones who shape our lives,
And guide us on our way.

Sufyaan Ishaq (14)

Mother

Hey Mother, hey Mother,
You are just the best for me.
You always make me happy,
When I am sad.

Hey Mother, hey Mother,
You are just the best for me.
Wherever I go, I will never forget,
The sweet memories with you.

Hey Mother, hey Mother,
You are just the best for me.
Whenever I think about you,
I just go into a land of
Happiness and joy.

Hey Mother, hey Mother,
You are just the best for me.
When I feel lonely,
You are just the one and only,
Supporter in my life.

Hey Mother, hey Mother,
You are just the best for me.
Because of your knowledge and support,
I did all the achievements.

Thank you for all the support,
And confidence you gave me.
Hey Mother, hey Mother,
You are the only one,
The best in my life forever.

Abheer Shetty (10)

Saudade

They say that Dad is a girl's first love
And indeed, I truly admired you.
You are clever and tall,
Charismatic and all
And you taught me why the sky
Seems blue.

I can't recall,
But I'm pretty sure
That I wanted to be just like you.

I remember asking you about all that's under the stars,
About dark oceans, plants, planes and Mars,
I remember asking you why, when and how,
About things that I've learnt by now.

I remember you calling me 'Snowdrop'.
I remember the good times,
But I remember your lows.
I remember I always used to say
That I love you as far as counting goes.

I am very proud to have the same brain,
And I see it when they say that I have your eyes.
I guess that genetics played a good part,
But there's one thing I'll never mention to you...

I'm glad I don't have
A bittersweet heart.

Naomi Haras (16)

Tilly Ramsay: The Superstar

She is a crazy lady,
But she is not lazy.
She has many a book,
She is a great cook.
Often cooking up a storm,
But to her, this is the norm!

She is my idol,
Partly, because she knows survival.
She is very funny,
Especially when with her mummy.
In some ways, she and I are alike,
Maybe together we could ride a bike.

She is brave,
But she is not afraid.
She is very persistent,
And also very resilient.
She is a person who is strong,
To her family, she does belong.

She has lots of good friends,
And does not need to make amends.
She has a heart of gold,

Which often she is told.
She shares her love,
With those that mean the most.

She is inspiring to all of us young ones,
Often baking yummy buns.
She has cooking competitions with her dad,
When he loses, it makes him mad!
Around the world, she reaches far,
Because she is a superstar!

Poppy Wright (8)

Aunty Angela

Her name is Aunty Angela
She is the best
She sits on top of
All the rest

She's like a hero
She has super strength
She never gives up
She can run a really long length

She is happy and playful
Joyful and fun
When she feels like it
She can really run

She is amazing
And really brave
With a swimsuit
She can swim in a really cold lake

On her head
Is long black hair
When something goes wrong
She is really fair

Sometimes
She spins me around

As she does it
She makes a funny sound

Her job is to help people
If they feel sad
It makes them feel
Not quite as bad

And now you can clearly see
Why my Aunty Angela
Is so important to me.

Ellie Liston (8)

Dad

Daring and determined, my dad stands tall,
Always there to catch me if I fall,
Devoted and caring, his love never ends,
Dedicated to family, his time he spends.

Adventurous spirit, he leads the way,
Dynamic and strong, he brightens each day,
Driven to succeed, he sets the bar high,
Dependable and wise, his guidance never dies.

My favourite person, my hero and friend,
A rock of support on whom I depend,
With his kind heart and loving ways,
He inspires me to live my best days.

In his footsteps, I strive to follow,
Determined to succeed, never to wallow,
For in his love and endless care,
I know I'll always have someone to share.

So here's to my dad, my guiding star,
A person whose love will take me far,
For in his embrace, I find my place,
And in his love, I'll always embrace.

Fatimah Rafiq (13)

The Key To My Heart

Every night I lie in bed,
I thank God for how the day went.
He made red kites,
And made the sun shine bright,
He even created the dark night.

He is with me all day long,
And is never wrong.
God also gave us all a life,
He gives me all my courage and strength,
To an unbelievable length.

He has a strong bond with all of us humans,
Which lasts as long as possible.
I go to church and sing hymns,
And remember when he sacrificed his life for all our sins.

He lit up my life from the day I was born,
And will carry me through the heavy storms.
He even takes me on precious tours,
He even gave lions and other creatures the ability to roar.

I thank the Lord for all he has done,
He keeps my life warm and shining like the sun.
He keeps me going day and night,
And only then, I will keep shining bright.

Lazzaro Pasquariello (12)

Imran Khan

Imran Khan, a name that echoes far and wide,
A man of passion, courage and pride,
A cricketer, a philanthropist, a politician,
A leader who inspired a nation.

He fought for justice, for the rights of the poor,
With a vision to build a better Pakistan for sure,
He stood for honesty, transparency and integrity,
And won the hearts of people with his sincerity.

He faced many challenges, but never gave up,
With determination and perseverance, he climbed to the top,
He proved that with hard work and dedication,
One can achieve greatness and make a difference in the nation.

Imran Khan, a true hero of our time,
Whose legacy will continue to shine,
A symbol of hope for the youth and the old,
A leader whose story will always be told.

Aliza Khan (9)

My Special Person

My special person is not just special but she is also one of my superheroes,
When my heart feels sorrow, she always gives me a hug to lift my lows,
Every time I am frustrated with something, she is there to help me with my problems,
Even when I am struggling, she is there to cheer me on,
She knows us better than we know ourselves,
She welcomes friends and family with delightful meals,
Once on a plane journey, a woman fainted and she came to save the day,
Being a nurse makes her everyone's superhero because 'not all heroes wear capes,' they say,
Her love encircles me like a warm hug on a cold day, you see,
Because she is the most important person to me,
She is my world, even if the population was zero,
My special person is not just special but she is also my superhero.

Ella Whetton (11)

Poem For My Mother

My mother is the best,
She can't keep up with my mess,
Nevertheless, she loves me no less.
She works really hard day and night,
To make sure my future is bright.
She helped me with my 7 times tables,
And now I know them off by heart.
One day when I grow up,
I want to thank her for never giving up.
My mother,
Others do have them but my mom is by far the best.
Teaches me new things each and every day.
Has a love that never goes away.
Elevates me in every possible way.
Reassures me when I'm in doubt.
Smart, strong and sincere,
Are just a few ways to describe my best friend, my mother.
That is the poem about my mom,
But just remember that my mom is the best,
And no one can beat her.

Lexi-Rae Duffy (9)

My Best Friend

B illions and trillions of people would want a bestie like mine, and I'm sure in every way.

E verything about her is fun, lovely and crazy!

S he is a little bit dumb though but our friendship is still amazing because when the other one is sad, the other cheers them up.

T ogether, we are unstoppable and we are the best ever.

F ighting has never happened to us before which is really

R are in friendships like ours.

I have been besties with her for over a year now, and I know it's not a lot, but we know

E ach other like the palms of our hands!

N either of us has ever talked badly about the other, and if you ask us, we

D o love each other like sisters!

Nadini Parevigodage (10)

My Idol

My idol is my mum,
She is the best,
She believes I can become,
Whatever I choose,

She always cares,
It's always important,
No matter the conditions,
She meets them all,

She is invincible,
Forgets all the others,
Her effect is irreversible,
She always cares,

My heart melts like snow,
When she leaves my side,
Always in tow,
My love for her,

She doesn't care,
What anybody says,
I don't need a prayer,
I have her,

She tries her best,
And she is stubborn,

I'm so blessed,
To have a mum like her,

She is the best,
I said that twice,
I'm just so impressed,
How much she cares,

I love her with an unreal love,
That grows bigger every day.

Alexandra Molina Greene (13)

Dear Bay Tree

Dear Bay Tree,
You are evergreen.
Always in our postage-stamp-sized garden
Branches dancing with the wind
A sparkle of life
In the gloomy grey city.

Your clusters of seed feed
The troopers who bring colour
To this cloudy cluttered yard:
Blackbirds. Tits. Squirrels.

You started as a seed
In some garden centre before even I
Came into being. You held on
Battled disease
Paving stones
Pets
Buildings
Foxes
When next door's eucalyptus had to be removed
We just smiled and pruned you.

You've seen bikes,
Scooters,
See-saws,

Sheds,
Grass.
Houses grow larger,
Lofts go up,
Generations come and go.
Yet steadfast, you remain.

I'm planting a kiss on your waxy leaves.
Thank you, dear bay tree
And all the little things in our lives
For always being there.

Leya Gross (14)

Sarah Paulson

Sarah Paulson, a star so bright
Her talent shines with every sight
On the stage or on the screen
Her performances leave us in a dream

From American Horror Story to The Goldfinch
Her range is vast, her characters distinct
She embodies each role with grace and skill
Leaving us captivated, thrilled and still

Her beauty, though stunning, is not her only draw
For her depth and complexity are what leave us in awe
From her nuanced expressions to her powerful voice
Sarah Paulson is a talent we should all rejoice

With each role she takes on, she proves her worth
As one of the greatest actresses of our time on Earth
So let us bask in the glow of her talent so bright
For Sarah Paulson is a star in our sight.

Amber Urquhart (12)

My Inspiration

My idol, the one I look up to,
Is a being of grace and virtue.
Their presence fills my heart with hope,
And in their footsteps, I strive to cope.

With wisdom that surpasses years,
And kindness that wipes away tears,
They guide me through the ups and downs,
And lift me up when I feel down.

Their strength and courage never waver,
In the face of any danger,
And I am in awe of their might,
As they lead with vision and insight.

Their spirit shines so bright and clear,
A beacon for all to draw near,
And I am grateful every day,
To have their guidance on my way.

My idol, my inspiration,
A model of dedication,
I aspire to be like you,
And in your path, I will pursue.

Aliza Sherazi (13)

Warrior

For Mum

You worry too much,
That is what they will say,
And maybe,
Just slightly,
It might be a little bit true,

But when your pen traces the paper,
And out glides your signature:
Twisting roads etched in ink -
I suddenly see the link.

The maps you admire,
The value you see in the knowledge of a location
Comes from a certain place.

The satisfaction that comes with a revelation
Can only truly be known by someone as knowledgeable as
you;
There is real reward in finding a fact
When the things left to know are so very few.

The maps you've travelled,
The places you point out,
You tell me about because you see
How fruitful knowledge can always be.

You worry too much,
But then again

You only want us to know
How much further we can go.

Ella Guy (16)

Them

My dog,
One of the best familial love.
He sits there waiting for my love.

He stares into my eyes, manipulating me
In a good way.
It's his way of communicating.

How can a furry friend help?

What if his time ticks and it goes *click-clack?*
It's coming closer to him
Leaving me
Cold, desolate, surrounded by nothing but the guilt
Of nothing
I've never done anything unforgivable

What if he feels drained?
What if he feels he's not enough?
What if he feels distressed?
Because of me.

Loyal, he is.

How do I know how he feels,
About me?
Does he feel enlightened by small acts,
Like us?

I adore him.
I want him to know.
But how?

I will never know.

So will he?

Laura Szwarc (13)

My Mother's Love

There is nothing like your mother's love
She has loved you since day one
I was welcomed into this world with unconditional love
And nothing will ever come in the way of that
She loved me before I even knew what love was about
Even through the temper tantrums and teenage troubles
I may not always be the nicest to *her*
But no matter what, we still love each other
For thirteen years, *she* has loved me
There is nothing worse than the pain I caused *her*
For *she* has shown me true love
And *she* will continue to until the end of time
That is why I will always look up to her.

Ailsa Thain (13)

Young Idol

I admire the way you don't care
The stupid dance you do when they stare
The way in which you eat
Without the look of defeat!

I wish I could be you, my younger self
You know, the kid who still believed in elves
The one that could run around naked
Without looking at his body all hated!

You always wished to grow older faster
But now you are just one big disaster
Each day blends into one
Live a little - just run!

You were always different and out of sorts
But you never allowed others' reports
To destroy you from being you
And that's special, boo!

Now society has crushed that little hope
That once helped you cope
So be free little me,
And just be
One with the sea!

Oliver Bracebridge-Henderson (15)

Overload

His enemy's fear was his only desire
Burning like an arrow set on fire
The melodic screams of a symphonic choir
Only made his desire burn higher.
Fields of green turned to flint and lead
Every soul he glanced at fell and bled
A man's life should be carefully tread
For he is risking imminent death.
Lust to greed, and greed to lust
His civilisation merely turned to dust
And all they could do is look in disgust
At the man they thought they once could trust
His enemy's fear was his only desire
But yet that desire quickly outgrew him
Now his memory by the day grows drier
And as dead as the people that knew him.

Lewis Howitt-Jones (15)

Sally Goodden

One of the people I admire is an artist,
She is an animal artist and realist,
Sally Goodden teaches others,
And helps them to become artists and art lovers.

This professional artist always had a passion for nature,
For many years, Sally was an illustrator,
She has a degree in scientific illustration,
Sally developed adding vibrancy to her animal portrait
commissions.

She focuses on capturing the animal's energy and character
in the eyes,
As well as discussing colour and styles to create beautiful
work for clients to buy.
These are the reasons why she inspires me.
However, the biggest reason why she is my idol is because
she inspires me to be an animal artist.

Sadie McSharry (11)

My Big Sister

My big sister is a quiet soul
But when she is with me
She is brave and outgoing
Always carrying the conversation

My sister isn't famous
But when we're together
To me, she is a famous artist
Whose art is viewed all over the world

My sister isn't a teacher
But when she is with me
She's a mentor
Teaching me the way of life

My sister isn't rich
But when she is with me
She is always buying me sweets
And giving me food

My sister is an ordinary person
But to me, she is outstanding
And I aspire to be like her
Every single day.

Margaret Armstrong (13)

My Twin

My twin is pretty, smart and cool,
I sometimes wish I was like her too.
Hiding in her shadow, the pain comes to me,
That I'm not like her, as I am just me.
I told my mum one day, you see,
That I hate myself (more than anything).
My mum replied, with the softest voice,
"Is that your real and final choice - to be like her?"
Oh *yes!* Oh *please!*" I replied with instant glee.
My twin came in, looking surprised.
And then said this, with great delight -
"You are pretty, you are great.
Don't even say that to my face!"
I smiled to myself and look very pleased,
Knowing that I have a great twin who's so kind to me...

Raazia Syeda (12)

Amazing Grace

This poem is about
My amazing 15-year-old cousin, Grace.
As her name states, she is a virtue.
I am so grateful to have her in my life,
She cuts through her condition like a knife.
She works so hard in everything,
She *can* do anything!
She's been through sooo much,
She pursues her dreams like no one else.
She is herself,
She doesn't just sit on the shelf like an elf.
She is a fighter,
She always tries to be brighter.
She is so thoughtful and selfless,
And she is far from helpless.
She is like a big sister to me.
Grace if you're reading this, I truly mean this!

Maya Oxborrow (10)

Painted Idol

Placed upon a golden throne
Glistening in the beams of sunlight,
He stands in the centre of my vision
The epitome of hubris and pride.

We stand and respect,
Salute and bow before the throne
Upon which He is seated,
Beneath the crushing blue skies.

Heat rolls off and wavers slightly.
His brows dip into a deep furrow.
Displeased, he slumps further into His throne of gold
As it melts,
Melts,
Melts as gold should not.

Our idol falls,
Tips off the edge of his seat
And it is done.
He steels His gaze as the paint chips,
Exposing an ashy grey that lies beneath.
The statue topples and He is downed,
Kneeling before our feet,
As we had once knelt at His.

Katie Walker (16)

A Tennis Legend

A brave and bold man on the tennis ground,
With fierce backhands and good rebounds.

His right hand is strong that sets him apart,
Winning Grand Slams breaks his opponents' hearts.

His racket is aggressive like thunder in the sky,
He hits the balls and makes them fly.

No challenge is too great for him and his passion never stops,
He has been with legends on the ground and has reached the top.

Novak Djokovic from Serbia is a true inspiration,
With the power of might and great determination.

He is a top name in his fraternity,
A champion of tennis for eternity.

Adrika Tewari (8)

My Mommy

My mommy is not very tall,
But she is the best mommy of all.
When I'm hungry and very sad,
She makes me yummy spaghetti and now I'm glad.
My mommy is so special, she is one of a kind,
She is the dearest and sweetest you will ever find.
When I was born, I was little and meek,
My mommy cared for me until I was not so weak.
My mommy is a good listener and she is so funny,
She is so calm and sweet just like honey.
Now I am at school, I'm a big boy,
To my mommy, I am such a joy.
Mommy, you are so special, you are like a dove,
You bring happiness to my world and so much love.

Alex Hall (9)

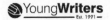

I Wish It Were Me

She smiles back at me, a sick sort of grin,
Mocking and cruel, twisting across her skin,
Everything I want to be, yet nothing I am,
Then the door closes and she's gone with a slam.
Though she's never away, not truly, not ever,
My own personal hell, a tragic endeavour,
My eyes flicker shut and I see her right there,
Nevertheless, if she looks back, I am quite unaware.
The real reason she follows, that she's always around,
Quiet and watching, there's never a sound,
Is that she is me, and that I am her,
Be as it may, shown as it were.
My cursed reflection, now just left be,
Oh, I wish, my darling, I wish it were me.

Aimee Wainwright (16)

LJ B

She brought me into this world.
She taught me to smile,
To laugh,
To love.
She taught me that I am enough.

She went through hell and back,
And never let her golden heart crack.
Whenever I need her most, she holds me close.

When the world comes crashing down around me,
She showers me in love.
Like rain showers down on the cracking, dried-up earth.

We share a middle name,
We share laughs and jokes.
She's the person who protects me,
When she knows it matters most.

There's no one I'm more proud of,
There's no one I love more.
There's nobody who knows me better,
Or who I'll ever need more.

Katie Bond (16)

Her Amber Eyes

For my best friend

I am alone,
I am silent, unloved and crying,
I stand while the darkness overwhelms me,
I just felt like dying,

But *she* picked me up,
She welcomed me while others would just disagree,
And I'd stare into her amber eyes,
And she'd stare at mine,
And I would smile,

And I would smile a smile of pure happiness,
While she would run along with me,
And make me happy every day,
With her, I was content,
And I asked her if she wanted to be my best friend,
And she never left me in the end,

I was oh so delighted,
I felt like a new time had just begun,
And again, I looked into her amber eyes,
But with no fear this time.

Onyinyechi Treasure Ndukwe (10)

The Squad

E is my heart, so kind and true,
He's smart and funny,
With eyes of blue.

L is sassy, fun and wise,
She's my best friend,
But Satan is disguise.

J is goofy, silly but kind,
He can burp the alphabet,
Always has something crazy in mind.

M is unique, with laughter for days,
She is my dancing queen,
And together, we slay.

These are my friends,
My laughter, my smile,
My confidence, my personality.
They're very special, you see,
And they are very important to me.

Willow-Rose Smith (11)

People I Admire

People I admire
Are women and men
And they inspire
The world is harmonised again

Cousin has battled through
Cancer at two
He did survive
He is one of the lucky few
And now he can thrive
The world is okay again

Father and his woodwork
With a hammer and a chisel
Mother and her handiwork
With some thread and a needle
The world is confident again

A friend has operations
A skin graft as well
He needs to have his sedations
He says it hurts like hell
The world is brave again

People I admire
Are women and men

And they inspire
The world is harmonised again.

Sophie Thomas (12)

Cat

Her sleek, shiny fur,
The rumble of her purr,
Her long, weaving tail.
Those soft, padded paws,
Hide her sharp claws,
This is how she starts her tale.

Her glinting green eyes,
How she jumps, how she flies,
See her body twisting.
Eternally fearless,
And always tearless,
See her body turning.

Her black, damp nose,
The elegant pose,
That appeared whenever she sat.
Her pointed, sensitive ears,
How swift she appears,
For this is the exquisite cat.

Her sleek, shiny fur,
The rumble of her purr,
Her long, weaving tail.

Those soft, padded paws,
Hide her sharp claws,
This is how she ends her tale.

Emilia Abaraviciute (10)

My Mum

From pub work to painting,
From late nights to creating,
My mum is my hero and nothing is changing.
She helped me to walk, talk and eat,
Ever since I was by her feet.
Four kids and thriving,
She is still shining.
A smile that lights up the sky,
Providing comfort when I cry.

Own business in hand,
I will never understand,
How one woman can be so grand.
Steadfast she is always to
Make sure I never fall fast.
Teaching me lessons about
How to live and be.
Allowing me to be free.
Her strength enduring,
Her advice always sustaining.
My mum is my hero and nothing is changing.

Faith London (14)

My Idol, Albert Einstein

Although his attitude towards learning could have been better,
Albert Einstein was smarter than many others who were way older.

He amazed people with his theory about light being a particle,
(Which explains why when it's shattered through rain, it makes a rainbow).

Knowledge was his aim,
Physics was his game.
Had two wives (one was his cousin),
Didn't have many children (three less than half a dozen).

Although his attitude towards learning could have been better,
Albert Einstein surpassed many people way smarter.

Okubotin Glory Cocodia (10)

William Shakespeare

In 1585,
That's when he was alive,
He wrote plays
And had a habit to amaze.
He made people think,
Opened their eyes
To see him how he was
A romantic in disguise.
He wrote a tragedy
About a man with a skull
His plays were never ever dull.
From murder and death
To fairies who sparkled
He never failed to tell a tale,
The man of law was one of many,
They would pay a single penny
To watch his shows and what they told.
And although he died
He lives on alongside
His poems and plays to this day.

Kara Rae Morgan (12)

Who's The Role Model?

From role models to family
No one is the same
They may all be different
But they have similar flames
From being strong to being kind
Their powers are all magnificent.

We're almost on our way to choose
Which one is the best
But let us dwell on the choices
So we don't fall for a ruse
We're almost there, just wait a little more
But now the time has come, I've chosen someone.

I'm sorry but I can't tell you who it is
But maybe next time when we meet again.
On second thoughts, maybe I should tell you,
The person is... *Albert Einstein!*
No one is the same.

Michael Olufemi (11)

N.M.

An idol is someone greatly admired,
Or loved by their fans.
Many people could fit under this category.
I chose someone who is my life,
And who knows I love them,
But I need to tell them more.
This person cares about others' opinions,
But not enough to change for anyone.
This person shows me love and safety at all times,
They have taught me to love me for me,
And to forget anyone who doesn't.
It doesn't seem like a lot as a viewer,
But as a participant, they have inspired me
To love and care the way they do.

Gracie Chapman (13)

God Is The Greatest

We don't sleep, we don't eat
We study, we listen
Sell yourself for the school system

We're seen as adults, yet treated like children
We're supposed to live our best life, yet end up living our worst
Sell yourself for the school system

Let Him guide you through this trouble
Let Him guide you to success
Sell yourself for the school system

When they trouble you, let Him know
Let Him care for you, you will be the success
Sell yourself for the school system

You want to be the greatest
Please Lord, give me a sign, should I do more?
Sell yourself for the school system.

Zahra Ahmed (13)

My Idol Will Always Be My Mummy

My idol has always been there for me,
Through the darkest times, they have helped me see,
Guided me through a world still so unknown,
They have never left me feeling alone,
They always nurture me and hold me close,
Reward my success and inspire my hope,
Tend to my bruise and wipe my teary eye,
Whenever our adventures go awry,
Once we are home again and snuggled up,
We make hot chocolates and cakes in a cup,
Climb under blankets and watch a movie,
Or point out our world's natural beauty,
Clothes me; feeds me; washes me when I'm muddy,
My idol will always be my mummy.

Beth Lamin (14)

My Mom Is My Superhero

My mom is my superhero,
There is nothing she can't do,
She washes all the dishes at such great speed,
All clean through!

She gathers all the dirty clothes,
And hikes to the top,
She gets the job done,
And finishes with a dance with the mop.

She plays with me and my siblings,
Like a jungle hide-and-seek,
And when she finds us,
We get a tickle treat!

My mom is my superhero,
There is nothing she can't do,
I love her so much,
I'm her biggest fan,
That is so true!

Haadiyah Davis (9)

My Favourite Uncles

I love my uncles
Uncle Immy is funny,
He buys us toys,
He buys us pizza!
He puts songs on in his car,
When he takes us for a ride.
Uncle Mohsin gives me chewing gum.
He wrestles with us,
And throws us on the bed.
He drives really fast in his car!
He plays video games with us,
And buys us presents.
Uncle Faisal plays games with us,
He picks us up and throws us down,
He wrestles with us,
He lets us play on his exercise bench,
He lets us play scary video games,
And he gives us sweets!
I love my uncles!

Mustafa Mahmood (5)

Uno, Dos, Tres - I Idolise You Nonetheless

My love sits tight up on a windowsill,
A love so grand, my hand lifts up my quill.
Fumble a word or two; perfection is
Tightly wrapped inside the words of language;
My quill could write in Spanish, Gaelic, Hind-
Immerse me with your beauty. Hidden doors
Open its conch shell shouting out loud and
My love dares to drop its jaw onto the floor.
I am moved by humans' existence in our globe,
One we share through the words of our love,
Gather a page into the many worlds.
Stop. Admire the seven million tongues.

Alec Bullett (17)

Orb

A wild woman who lived a wild life,
A bold girl with bold dreams,
With a passion for fashion,
She rips and sews the seams.

Bondage, plaid, the infamous orb;
Vivienne Westwood,
A designer to be adored.

Eccentricities and a striking world view,
Such is the inspiration for a flashy band or two.
X-Ray Spex - in '76 - with her bondage pants,
And the '75 Sex Pistols, who gave rock a chance.

A dubious making,
Those bizarre fabric commodities.

Brightly controversial,
But she was loved.
And so the lettuce-loving punk lived,
To the end with peaceful oddity.

Laura Ann Houlder (12)

My Mother

M y mother is an absolutely fair and just hero

Y our mum is probably your hero too!

M y mum is caring, loving, kind, generous, hardworking and a chef

O n occasions, whilst working at school, she shares good talks with children about mothers

T his year, I love my mum *more* than last year

H appy, joyful, smiley, helpful and the best!

E ncouraging words are *always* on my mum's lips

R espect is one of the things my mum has taught me from the age of five.

Muhammed Khizar Khan (8)

The Best Sister Ever

This poem is for my amazing sister
Every moment she's gone, I miss her
She is very funny and smart
Also, she has a big heart

She supports me with my work
She makes me laugh and smirk
When I'm down, she's always there
Finding a sister like this is very rare

She is always caring and kind
The best sister I could ever find
She is a shining star
Without her, I wouldn't go far

She is one to inspire
Definitely someone I admire
It feels like she's from high above
That's her, that's the sister I love.

Naoise Dunne (10)

Thank You, Carol

I just want to thank you for always being there,
And teaching me all I need to know
It's due to you, I live my life true and fair
You believe in me however far I need to go
And, Carol, it's because of you I feel free
From desire and all that it means
I would not be able to, just me
And I trust you since what I have seen
My time in life has been an absolute pleasure
From ballet to tap and any other
And it's all for my leisure
Because of you, I found my sisters and brothers
We are family through thick and thin
Not having you would be a sin.

Elijah Conway (11)

Laura Ellen Anderson

L aura, Laura, Laura, you inspire me so much. You write
my favourite books like Rainbow Grey and Amelia Fang.

A nd you are a bright burning star making me want to
read and write books just like yours. Your

U nique way of writing is amazing, your books are funny
and full of suspense. I

R eally do love your books, Laura Ellen Anderson. I
appreciate the work you do for young readers.

A ll of the amazing stories you write, I love. Please keep up
the excellent work and write even more children's books.

Lucy Andrew (9)

I Love You, Mummy

I love your gorgeous smile,
That brightens up my day.
I love your loving hugs,
To help my worries drift away.
I love your personality,
Your joy lights up the world.
I love that you make me feel,
Like such a special girl.
I love your caring, young heart,
You're so kind and very fun.
I love how you look after us,
And how you're there for everyone.
I love your sense of humour,
When we spend time together.
I love you so much, Mummy,
You really are my best friend forever.

Samara Acton (11)

Now My Saviour From Above

Now my saviour from above
My nan, brave and beautiful,
Her special glistening eyes staring into my soul
Watching me from above,
As I do the greatest things and learn the greatest things,
Love is always floating around us,
I miss her loads, as do other people;
It is horrible losing a loved one.

You meant so much to me,
I know why Heaven called you,
I mean, why wouldn't they,
I wish you could have stayed, but it's time to let go,
The memories I have of you will always stay,
You may not be here,
But you're locked in my heart forever.

Billie-Marie Perry (11)

You Are My Hero

F ather, thank you for
A lways being there for me
T eaching me skills
H aving the biggest heart
E xpecting nothing but giving everything
R eally, you are the best.

In my world,
You are my hero.
When I falter,
You are strong.
When I lose my way,
You lead me.
When I hurt,
You hear what's wrong.
When I need a true example,
One to be my guiding star,
You are my source of light,
Reaching out,
From where you are.

Syed Muhammad Shahmir Hassan (11)

We Are Each Other's

It's a new day and my Amayah is happy
He makes me laugh
He shares his toys
He is my friend forever

We share adventures like holidays at the beach
We talk about cartoons
We both love eating crackers
He is my forever friend

On my journey in life,
Amayah and I will be teaching and learning.
On my journey in life,
Amayah and I will grow and play, being boys.

On my journey in life,
Amayah and I will have fun always.
On my journey in life,
Amayah and I will pick each other up!

We are each other's idols.

Theodore Palmer-Clarke (3)

Mother's Day Poem

H ow lovely you are
A joyful, happy sight
P lease be mine
P retty and nice
Y es, Mummy

M others are the best
O range and blooming
T he best mum ever
H ow much I love you
E very time you go to work, I kiss you
R eading with Munira every day
S melling like roses that bloom

D ays never end without you
A nytime I'm lonely, I'll look for her
Y ou are the best.

Uzma Sebagala (7)

My Mum

The person I admire most,
Is my mum, not trying to boast,
She cares for me,
And lets me be.

She cared for me for more than a year,
Now, her love for me is really clear,
She lets me play,
But not all day.

To her, education is key,
The person she made smart is me,
She wants me to be my best,
More than you can guess.

This is my mum, my sun,
My success orbits around Mum,
There's nothing more for me to say,
But Mum is brighter than the sun.

Katie Yun Jue Hu (10)

She Is A Superstar

She is very pretty, her face is a work of art
Her smile can light up any room, even in the dark
She is successful and very kind in the heart
Millie Bobby Brown is a superstar

She is inspiring and wonderful, she never gives up
She is an actor, she is kind and has a really cute pup
She loves making jokes and is really funny
And when she goes outside, it suddenly turns sunny

Millie is the best a person can be
If you want to be kind, Millie has the key
Who is amazing? It's Millie Bobby Brown
Who is the best? Millie has the crown.

Sofia Christophe (11)

My Big Fella

M usic is in the air when we are together
Y ou are my best friend

B ig hugs and kisses every day
I f I need your help, you are always there for me
G lauco is your name and playing with me is your favourite game

F abulous and creative are your best qualities
E ven when I am sad, you make me laugh
L oving you is so simple
L aughing is easy when I am with you
A gain, again and again, I'd want a daddy like you.

Sofia Vallarino (8)

The Person I Admire

The person I admire
Has more qualities than I can count.
Though she remains humble,
She really is so great!
She's creative, clever and kind,
Outgoing, confident and fair.
The person I admire
Has her cup half full.
She's awesome in every way.
If she'd just look at what she has,
She'd see it all so clear.
The person I admire
You have one just like her.
You also know someone
Who has so much to share!
Look no further than the mirror,
There's so much you can be!
The person I admire
Is myself, I'll now admit!

Mimi Gross (16)

Dennis And Dad!

Dennis and Dad,
Without them, I'd go mad,
It would just be plain sad,
Without Dennis and Dad.

Dad drives a great white van,
With Dennis at his side,
It's a bumpy ride,
Dennis and Dad.

Dennis is my brother,
I wouldn't wish for another,
But when he's paired with Dad,
He can become very bad!
Dennis and Dad.

Dad is my dad,
Dennis is my brother,
Without them, I'd go mad,
And become very sad,
Dennis and Dad!

Rose-Petal Needham (9)

I Love You, Mum

Mum, I love you so much
And think about you
All the time and every day.

You lift me up when I am down
You always make me smile
I just love when you're around.

You empower me to live my life
To be the best that I can be
To conquer and overcome obstacles.

I want to thank you
For always being there for me
For making sure that I am well cared for.

Thank you for your friendship
And the love you've given me
I love you, Mum!

Chika Onukwuli

M... U... M

Here is **My Unique Mother**...
A crazy teammate in my board games
Who makes yummy dishes with nicknames
She loves paintings always
And makes the best painting cocktails
I like to see my mom dance
Because it reminds me of mantles drifting in water
She is my partner in crime in clues
She loves and supports me and knows how to choose
And that is **My Unique Mother**...

Aaryan Madhav (9)

My Mum

My mum is very kind,
She has a brilliant mind!

She loves me with all her heart,
She is very smart!

She makes yummy food,
She is never in a bad mood.

My mum takes me on holidays,
Sometimes in mountains, sometimes in bays.

Me and my mum like to cuddle,
We like to jump in muddy puddles.

I like to sleep on my mum's pillow,
Me and my mum like a tree called 'Willow'.

We love each other,
She is the best mother!

I want to be like her when I am older,
Intelligent, kind, stronger,
And a lot more bolder!

Shreyashi Sinha (6)

Perfect

People compare bikes to cars,
Skirts to jeans and cats to dogs,
But no one compares anything
To a girl that loves a guy like a father,
Looks up to him in a way
That can only be summed up with one word - Perfect.
Perfect is the only word.
You know all that person's flaws,
You know all their mistakes,
But don't care,
As all those little errors make them perfect.
The only thing that matters is that they treat you
With nothing but love and support.

Allie Murray (14)

Xolo, My Idol

Xolo Maridueña or Miguel from Cobra Kai,
Wait, Cobra Kai never dies!

All the time, I watch him act,
He is absolutely amazing,
Now, that's a fact!

He is one of the best,
A middle parting on his head,
I swear he is always wearing a vest.

Miguel, he is known as,
Oh, what great acting skills he has.

I guess now I have to say goodbye,
But before I do, I have one thing to say...

Xolo is such an amazing guy!

Kai Grainger (11)

My Superheroes

My superhero is gone,
My superhero disappeared,
My superhero went missing,
My superhero was never there.

My superhero could be kind,
But also lie,
They could bake me a pie,
With poison inside,
They could listen to my secrets,
But tell everyone.

My superhero is here,
My superhero is perfect,
My superhero was always close,
My superheroes start with an M and a D,
And look around 103,
My superheroes are Mummy and Daddy!

Cayla Bright (10)

Ivan Ivanov

I have a brother named Ivan, Ivan Ivanov.
He has autism, but he is my superstar.
He is quite bizarre,
But he never fails to make my day.

I have a brother named Ivan, Ivan Ivanov.
He has autism, but he is kind.
He has a great mind,
And he cares a lot.

I have a brother named Ivan, Ivan Ivanov.
He has autism, but I love him.
He is cute and lovely,
And the rise of my family's bad days.

I love Ivan Ivanov.
He is confident,
Brave,
And always amazed.

I love Ivan Ivanov.

Dilyana Ivanova (10)

Mom

Mom, you are my *first*,
First face, smile, smell, love.
You've taught me to be *me*
And to stick to what I believe!

Mom, the memories we've made,
Put a cheerful smile on my face.
Even through our ups and downs,
You've stuck around.

Mom, you have made a sacrifice for me,
9 months going on 10 years.
Beside me, holding me, loving me,
All I can do is never stop showing you the love I have for *you!*

Cattleya Fahmi (9)

That's My Mum

She helps me when I'm feeling low
That's my mum
She is learning every day and I love watching her grow
That's my mum

She can get stressed
That's my mum
She'll always do her best
That's my mum

She's hardly ever mean
That's my mum
She will always be my queen
That's my mum

She doesn't tell lies
That's my mum
She will rise
That's my mum

She brings tears to my eyes
No more sad goodbyes
Whenever I need her, she will come
Because she's my mum!

Elodie Douglas (10)

My Auntie

A person that inspires me is...
(Don't tell anyone, but my favourite auntie).
She is a super coder, the strongest you can meet.
She'll help you with your homework 'cause she's smart.
Then you'll ace that test,
Then you'll see that she's really one of the best aunties.
Most of the time, she travels,
But we love her just as much,
But remember, if you have someone that inspires you,
Make sure you keep in touch.

Neferura Sukaina (9)

My Mum

My mum is disabled
And she tries anything
To make her feel
Able.

She is a lover and
A fighter
A trier and a carer.

Every day can be
Different
With new things to
Try.

She left work to focus
On her and me
Also occasionally has
Friends round
For tea.

Her tears make her
Stronger, even if it
May cause her
Pain.

My love for her
Is unimaginable.

Emelia Watts (11)

Someone That I Know

From the early hours of the morning
To the late hours of the night
There was only one person that I had in mind
This person was someone I knew all too well
Someone who was kind
Someone who loved themselves
They often shared stories about their life
Whether it was writing letters or riding their bike
A candle was lit for every time,
For every moment they felt alive
This is the person I know all too well
A person who I wished would love themselves
This person is me.

Archsiga Jeyakumar (17)

Powerful Pickford

You shoot,
You don't score,
Why?
It's him,
He's Pickford.

He's strong,
He's powerful,
He's tall,
He's cool,
His hands are like tongs,
And his dives are long.

He's England's,
The only one,
For he is super fun.

I'm a pre-teen,
Who watches the screen,
I have hopes and dreams,
And when I'm watching him,
He makes me believe.

Lylah White (11)

O Mangaka Ishinomori

O Mangaka Ishinomori,
The godfather of tokusatsu.
The legendary Shotaro Ishinomori,
Who revolutionised superheroes too.

O Mangaka Ishinomori,
Who incites a hero in us all.
And when the world gets scary,
Brings life to the warriors who'll never fall.

O Mangaka Ishinomori,
Your legacy lives on forever.
Your pen writes an eternal story,
As you inspire, no matter the endeavour.

Legendary Mangaka who'll be remembered,
Because 'heroes are forever'.

Noah Springthorpe (17)

My Hero, My Dad!

Dad, my hero, strong and true,
A guiding light to find my way through,
With every challenge, every mile,
Your love and support never fail to make me smile.

Your wisdom and helping hand,
Have helped me to grow and understand,
The world around me, the path ahead,
And how to face it with strength and stead.

So here's to you, my loving dad,
For all the joy and fun we've had,
I thank you from the bottom of my heart,
And know that we will never be apart.

Gracie-Leigh Bentley (12)

My Mum Is Super Special

My mum is super special
She means a lot to me
There's not a moment in the day
I cease thinking about her love for me

My mum smells like nature
Like meadows and trees
In my mind, her blood flows green
And her hair is a beautiful blooming tree

My mum's hug is like a blanket
That feels soft and warm
When I feel her arms around me
It's like a barrier protecting me from harm

My mum will always inspire me
To be the best I'll ever be.

Hana Gaspar (11)

Looking Down, Not Up

The best time of my life, summer '22,
The year I was blessed with not one but two.
Two little angels sent from above,
Joining our family and spreading their love.

Singing, playing and walking in the park,
With you in my life, it will never be dark.
Myla and Amiah, you're my love and desire.

My two little nieces, I love you to pieces.
Though I don't look up to you,
I have to look down,
Life is much better since you two came around.

Ava McCracken (11)

I Admire

I admire my mummy,
Her food is so yummy.
I like her curly hair,
And she is the one that will always care.

Her rosy cheeks are so nice,
And is always trying to be precise.
When something is hard, she keeps on trying,
She comforts me when I'm crying.

My mummy helps me to grow up great,
And she helps me when I'm in a state.
She is ever so kind,
And has a very good mind.

Zanna Eggertsen (9)

A Football Sensation

Dedicated to Leah Williamson

A football sensation,
That's what they say,
Always running around,
Having a game.

Happy at centre back,
And always on track,
Leah makes sure England's at their best,
Even if they're all being pests.

Leah is a star,
People at the bar,
Watching her match,
Making sure the goalie's ready to catch.

Leah is amazing,
She's a football sensation!

Eliza Ball (9)

My Mother

Mum, you are my sun,
Way up in the sky.
You shine light in the dark,
And lift me so high.
Mum, you are my rock,
My flower in spring.
My knight in shining armour,
My one true everything.
How did you do it, Mum,
All through the years?
Put up with my whining,
And all of those tears.
I love you forever,
My beginning and end.
Mum, you are a blessing,
A perfect best friend.

Rosie Oliver (15)

Carers

You have so much care to give,
Compassionate in what you do,
Looking after everyone - never off your feet,
Always on the go,
Checking in on those who are bedridden,
Chatting to all your patients,
Singing along to old songs,
Always full of care,
I admire the love and tender care you give,
Without you, who knows where they would be,
Always going above and beyond,
You have so much to give.

Daniel Murray (11)

Mummy!

You're my underwater treasure,
Found far beneath the surface.
No one else can find you,
You're an absolute pleasure.

You're a star in the night,
Way up in the sky.
Giving away your shine,
You're an absolute delight.

You're the grass in the field,
Very green and new.
You give me things with no strings attached,
You're my rock, you're my shield.

Isla Hobbs (9)

A Precious Mother

Mum, you've given me so much
Love from your heart
The warmth of your touch
The gift of life, you're a friend to me
We have a special bond which only
Comes from God
I'm sure you'll agree

As a child, I say, Mummy, I love you
Now, you're my mother so dear
I love you even more with each
And every new year

If I could have chosen
I would have picked no other
Than for you to be my lifelong friend
And precious mother.

Aizah Ramzan (11)

Izzy, My Big Sister

Izzy, my big sister, is so nice to me,
Oh Izzy, oh Izzy, you are so nice to me.

She is very kind when she is playing with me,
I see her every day.

She is very nice to me at school,
She helps me every day.

She helps me with my spellings,
When I practise them every day.

She tells me the time,
When I should wake up every day.

I love you very much, Izzy.

Ellie Underwood (6)

To Whom I Admire, Whom I Adore

All the people I admire,
Always there to inspire,
Whether it's a high or a low,
They'll always be there,
To nurture me as I grow,
I'll always be grateful to those I owe,
The thanks within me overflows
They've supported me from the start,
Even as time seems to dart,
I'll hold them close to my heart,
Even after we part,
There to watch me soar,
This is to whom I admire,
To whom I adore.

Ashley Watkinson (14)

My Teacher!

English, maths, science and others,
Anything you teach me,
Starts to make sense,
I'm sorry that we give you a hard time,
But that time is precious to me,
And I'll be happy that it's mine,
My teacher is one of a kind,
A kind that we all need and want,
This school is very lucky to have her,
Thank you for helping me have a smart mind!
Thanks to you, I have gotten better.

Aminah Faisal (10)

My Grandma, My Nani

She's cool, she's rad
She finds the good in bad
She's wrinkly and old
But it doesn't stop her being gold
She's my grandma
Nani, how beautiful you are
My grandma!
Do we have to live far?
Words can't explain how much I love you
So I dedicate this poem to...
My grandma!
Nani, how loveable you are
My grandma
She's my shooting star.

Harleen Hayer (12)

Grandma

She's a great friend, she is,
She inspires me with pleasure.
What a great grandma she is,
Having her is just like treasure.

She's fun to play with,
I love her with all my heart.
Even when I'm in a mood,
And not being very smart.

She's great to play with,
We're always having fun.
Playing around in the garden,
And smiling in the sun.

Brooke Hobbs (9)

My Daddy

My daddy is amazing
Better than all the rest
He makes me yummy pancakes
They really are the best
They are the most amazing
Pancakes the world has ever seen.
When I am scared, he cheers me up
And is never ever mean.
He makes me laugh with the stories that he tells
And doesn't get mad, even with my smells.
I love my daddy so much
To infinity and beyond
He is my chef, my tickle monster,
The best hero I've got!

Grayson O'Brien (7)

Allah

Of which 99 names,
The one who stays,
Looking over you all the time,
Loving you your whole life,
The almighty and the best,
Works without a rest,
Tests you every day,
Till you pass away,
A love 70 times more than your mother,
Allah is above all others,
And yet hates to see you suffer,
Made you from clay,
With love and in the best way,
Allah is here for you and will always be,
From day to day,
To history.

Maria Aitbaziz (14)

You Are

A poem for Grandpa

You are so many things,
You are a carpenter,
You are a husband,
You are a father.

You are a carpenter,
But that does not make you a man,
You are a man because
You are lion-hearted.

You are a husband,
But that does not make you loving,
You are loving because
You are gentle of soul.

You are a father,
But that does not make you true,
You are true because
You are honest of mind.

But most of all,
You are
Grandpa.

Rose Greiff (12)

Thank You, Mum

Thank you for making my lunch,
When I bite into my delicious sandwich, the lettuce goes *crunch!*
Thank you for ironing my clothes and tucking me into bed until I doze
Thank you for doing my hair each day, I treat it with care
Thank you for taking me to tap and ballet, I feel happy every day
I am very grateful to have a wonderful mum
Who plays with me in the sun!

Ava Katiyo (9)

For My Amazing Mum

Some people have idols,
Idols well known
But not all have to be
Sitting on a throne

My idol is my mum
She is my hero
Out of ten, I would give her
A big one, one zero

She's wonderful and kind
She's beautiful and nice
She's smarter than she'll ever know
And she gives the best advice

I would like to tell her,
That she is the best mum ever
And I will always love you
Forever and ever.

Imogen Buckle (12)

My Nana, My Hero

M other to everyone
Y oung at heart

N urturing nature
A lways putting others before herself
N ever-ending love
A mazingly awesome

M agnificent and motivational
Y ou're simply the best

H appy to help
E xcellent in every way
R esilient
O ne of a kind!

Daisy Langton (9)

My Cousin, Mila

Mila is my little cousin,
She is only one year old,
Even though she is still young,
She does what she is told.

She is a little cutie,
That I can't deny,
But when she doesn't get her way,
She will cry, cry, cry.

She likes to watch cartoons,
Her favourite one is Bing,
When it is on the telly,
She doesn't say a thing.

Lexie-Mai Collins (9)

My Big Sis

She's strong, smart and beautiful,
I always look up to her,
She loves gymnastics as well as me,
She goes upside down while tumbling,
Swings on the bars like a monkey
And balances on beams smiling and having fun,
I love her to the moon and back,
She loves animals, especially our cats,
We have three of them that she loves a lot,
My big sister is my hero and my best friend.
I love you! x

Sophie O'Sullivan (9)

Emily Idol

Herself - a poet
Private; cagey
Called egocentric

Called foolish
Loving, not cushy

Take the opportunity - the rights
Forever haunted by love
Emily, know, inspire

When mindset was foggy -
Words became
Why? Ask - she made new
Made forbidden true

Hope to feel
Hope to live
As she did to the fullest.

Jessica Stacey (11)

My Favourite Person

My favourite person is... take a guess!
I'll give you a clue, or two...
She likes to eat healthily, she likes to go for walks
She makes me pancakes for breakfast.
I like her because she looks after us,
She takes us to nice places
Like Grassington, Legoland and Aero Bounce.
She takes us on holiday and she is super-duper kind.
I love her so much!

Answer: My mummy.

Noor-Ul-Faatiha Mahmood (8)

Walking Beside Me

God created the world and me,
From animals to the tallest tree.
He made the charming day and night,
He even made my life so bright.

Without him, I'd be lost,
I'll never forget he died on the cross.
I always sing my favourite hymns,
Remembering he took away all my sins.

I'll never forget what he did,
Even though I am a kid.
As I grow older,
We will stand shoulder to shoulder.

Arabella Pasquariello (9)

When I Think Of Idols

When I think of idols,
Well, it's not what I believe,
So I sit here pondering,
Who the idol that comes to mind should be.
Then I realise nobody,
Having an idol is someone who you look up to
But before you look up to anyone else,
You have to look up to yourself.
If you idolise yourself,
You'll understand the world around you, see?
So, idols,
I imagine nobody - except me.

Daisy Goldman (12)

My Best Friend

My best friend, the girl who is always there,
But can never see her beauty.
The girl who would never judge,
But is scared of others' judgement.
The girl that has a heart of gold for others,
Yet doesn't treat herself with that gold.
She deserves everything good in the world,
As she isn't normally told.
But she must make that adjustment,
To love herself as much as I love her.

Poppy Raw (13)

Central Cee

C razy famous dude
E lectric Tesla whip, he's got 10
N ah, he's the best
T rapstar drip, he's got 10
R ap is his genre
A pair of MJs, he's got 10
L A Leakers freestyle

C ome on, he's the best, 10/10
E y, he's the best, 10/10
E y, he's the best, 10/10.

Riccardo Farinella (10)

Napoleon Bonaparte

He conquered,
He fought,
He invaded with thought.

He won't give up the cause,
He was powerful,
His army was strong,
But his navy was deficient.

His bravery was listed,
He was fearless and bold,
The townspeople thought he was a hero,
That wasn't old.

He was important,
He was truthful,
But when power went to his head,
He became dishonest.
He was Napoleon Bonaparte!

Zhuxi Pan (8)

My Stepdad

You weren't there when I was born but,
You stepped in when we needed you the most.
You make the best omelettes,
And best toast.
We are always laughing when you're around,
You tell the best jokes, just like a clown.
You work really hard every day,
But you still make time for fun and play.
You give me hugs when I'm sad,
I'm really happy that you're my dad.

Nathan Robb (9)

My Best Friend, Lily

She has the attitude
She's my best friend
I have the gratitude
And that's till the end

She's insane
And kind
Whereas I have a brain
And it's my mind

She's crazy
But she's mine
Her sister's called Daisy
And she's almost 9

She's 10
Her favourite place in England
Is the Big Ben

She's my bestie
But sometimes she tests me.

Olivia Grace (11)

My Mummy

My mum is my hero because she loves us equally.
Her favourite colour is blue and I painted a picture.
So many different colour blues
Her favourite sport is running and she likes the ukulele.
Whatever would I do without this amazing lady?
Tall and proud, happy and sweet
She is definitely a one-in-a-million sweet.
She is my hero and one of a kind.

Umme-Abiha Abid (9)

Mrs Roberts

Our teacher, Mrs Roberts,
She really likes yoghurts.

I really like it when she reads us a book,
But if we interrupt her, she gives us the look.

In class, if you are naughty and muck about,
Mrs Roberts will give you a really loud shout.

But I am a good boy and always try my best,
That's because my teacher is better than the rest.

Zayden Cavanagh (9)

David Walliams

D ahl is successful
A wful Auntie
V illain
I n the number one best sellers
D emon Dentist

W orld's Worst Pets
A mber
L augh out loud
L ovey Doveys
I mpossible to not laugh
A untie Flip (Bad Dad)
M r Big
S ally (Midnight Gang).

Muhammad Faheel Saqib (10)

Miss Jordan

Miss Jordan is amazing,
She's as great as can be.
She loves books and history,
Just like me!

She is a fantastic teacher,
And she's full of positivity.
I'm sad to say goodbye,
But I hope she will come back and visit me.

She is going to be an awesome author,
And I will look out for her name in lights!

Sophia Rood (8)

Heart

You are my dreams and never my fears,
You are my light and never my dark.
I listen to you with my ears,
You are my family, so I have your mark.

The sun rises and you have become wiser,
The sun has set and I have remembered what I forget.
We make you late for work,
And you take your lunch without a fork.
But...
It doesn't stop you from loving us.

Manahil Ishaq (10)

A Poem About Family

We share joy, peace and laughter,
In moments of tears and fear.
You're diamonds that can't be priced,
You're the consciousness in me.

Creasing my fears,
Healing my wounds,
You're never out of my heart's bounds.

Wishing me luck, giving me hope.
You pursue me into my future,
Making it as bright as it can possibly be.

Dominykas Krencius (11)

My Mum

You always know what's wrong even if I don't say,
You know how to help me when I lose my way.
You're always by my side,
With unconditional love that no one else can provide.
You always go the extra mile just to make me smile.
You're here, you're there, you are everywhere.
Thank you, Mum, for always being there.

Mia Sturla (15)

Sisters Before Misters

Sisters before misters, they say,
By the way, my older sister's name begins
With Kay and she was
One of the people who taught me
That horses go neigh.
I care about her, she cares about me,
That's why when she gets
A sir, he has to be the right guy for her
Because I don't want her to
Be heartbroken.

Brianna Chadwick (10)

My Mum

My mum is a beautiful woman
My mum always makes me happy
My mum goes out with me
My mum plays games with me
My mum always makes me feel safe
My mum always makes me feel better

My mum is brave and smart
My mum is strong

I admire my mum
I love my mum so much
I love my mum to the moon and back.

Mason Hicks (9)

My Mum

My mum doesn't hum,
But she likes honey,
As well as being funny,
Hmm, that is my mummy.

She makes me play ice hockey,
While I want to be a jockey,
Why, why? I ask her,
And then touch my cat's fur.

My mummy,
Wants me to draw a bunny,
But it's too sunny,
That's my mummy.

Luna Clark (7)

My Mum

You are an amazing teaching assistant at school,
The children in reception think you're cool!
You like to teach me Latvian,
When on a call with friends and family.
But when I get a word wrong,
You act like Grammarly.
You're always there for me when I'm in need,
You're always there for me in the lead.

Melisa Ciparsone-White (10)

My Grandad

M y superhero grandad
Y ou were my best friend

G randad, you were amazing in every way
R ain or shine, you were always there
A very special person
N ever will you be forgotten
D o you know I miss you loads
A nd
D o you know I will love you forever?

Maisie Taylor (11)

My Nanny Downstairs

My nanny is my favourite
My nanny is my mummy's mummy
I love my nanny to the moon and back
My nanny gives me big hugs and kisses
My nanny tells me the best jokes till our eyes water
My nanny is the best because she is my nanny
And you'll never get a nanny like mine
Because nannies are all different.

Alani Barmes (3)

Me And My Mummy

Me and my mummy play, play, play,
Me and my mummy play bounce,
Love and hop all together in the rain.

Me and my mummy dance and dance,
Me and my mummy, it's so much fun!

Me and my mummy cuddle at night,
Squeeze up tight in the night.
Me and my mummy kiss goodnight,
I love you, Mummy.

Rita Santonastaso (6)

My Mother

My mother
The most incredible
Human being
I could ever meet
From the way she cares
To the way she loves
And how she's
So selfless
Putting others first
Oh, how I love her
No one could ever
Be more superior
Than her
Oh, how her heart
Is like a star
Lighting up
The sky above
She's a lighthouse
Guiding me out
Of harm's way.

Anya Elliott (13)

Hulk, My Hero

Hulk is strong
He can lift the ground
And make the world a happy place
Wherever he goes
The Earth follows...

Hulk is strong
Like a Titan
His skin will lead the soil
His army will follow
He takes charge
The army will take charge

Hulk is strong
Hulk, my hero.

Darsh Desai (9)

My Daughter

The wind, the willow trees swaying in the night,
The waves, the boat rocking back and forth in the day,
No matter where, no matter when,
I will love you to the end.
Big or small, young or old,
You are my child.
Deep down within my inner self,
I'm the same as you in health and heaven.

Lucia Grilli (13)

My Super Dad

My dad's name is Sunny,
And he is very funny.
He loves cats and especially bats,
And he wears hats.

He plays football with me,
And drinks coffee and milk with me.
He gives me a hug and a kiss at night,
Switches off the light,
And says goodnight.

Love you, Dad.

Aaroush Puniyani (7)

Grandad

G randad, you are awesome!

R unning around the garden is more fun with you

A lways putting a smile on my face

N obody else is as awesome as you

D oing Lego is really fun with you

A ren't you so amazing!

D on't forget, I'll always love you.

Dexter Barrow (6)

Darkwing Duck

Darkwing Duck is a daring duck of mystery,
And a champion of what's right.

Airborne flyer,
Rescuing duck,
Kind duck,
Wise duck,
Very wise,
Intense duck,
Naive sidekick,
Grateful hero,
Dull hero,
Ultimate hero,
Clever hero,
Knowledgeable hero.

Andrew Popa (8)

Makaila, My Bestie

Makaila is the person I look up to,
She is very good in football shoes.
She runs as fast as the wind blows the sea,
She is always as kind as can be.
Makaila is the best person you could wish for,
She always has kindness to pour.
The pain that you feel,
Is easily healed,
By her inspiring words of wisdom.

Vera Krauchuk-Muzhiv (10)

A Poem About Mummy...

Mummy is beautiful inside and out,
She is my world without a doubt.
Mummy always brightens my day,
She always listens to whatever I say.
Mummy is always there for me,
She tells me to be the best I can be.
Mummy is so nice and sweet,
She makes me happy with a lovely treat.

Imogen Rowson (8)

Writers

Why choose just one? It's a world of opportunity,
Reading can be anywhere, do anything,
Stories take you to a whole new universe,
Treasure troves of limitless inspiring,
Every day transports you to a new place,
Rocky mountains, rivers of fantasy,
And sometimes I wonder, *could this be me?*

Henry Withnell (9)

Mummy

M y mummy is amazing, kind and caring

U nbelievably creative with all the crafts that she makes

M y mummy gives the best hugs and listens to my worries

M indful and helpful, she does so much for us

Y ou, Mummy, are the best, I love you oh so much!

Charlotte O'Brien (9)

Mum

A mother that is made of the purest diamond but her heart is real,
Eyes full of wondrous love,
Love to never be washed away,
No matter how many times she's cried,
To her, I'm like a crate full of coins and gems lost in the ocean,
Even when she's gone, her love will always be here.

Kairi Parry (10)

My Mommy

Jumping, skipping and feeling high,
Giggling and running under the blue sky.
Love is you, love is us,
What I am; the love of thy,
Always kind and always nice,
To tell you, Mommy, I feel a little shy,
Thanks for making my days the best,
Lots of kisses and I love you, that's why.

Aaron Aamir (6)

Daddy

The person that inspires me is my dad,
He's kind and helps me when I feel sad.
I love my dad so much, but sometimes he's at work,
Even when he's at home, he goes a bit berserk.
Dad's job is always getting bigger,
Sometimes he lets me go on his digger.

Myra Geldard (7)

Guess What I Am?

What is beautiful?
What is in the zoo and looks cool?
What is really cute?
What's sometimes mute?
What eats bamboo?
I eat and go.
What is fluffy?
It feels really puffy.
Which animal is white,
With a colour that's bright?
Guess which animal I am.

Answer: A panda.

Aisha Kausar (9)

It's Always Been Him

It's him
It's always been him
The looks we exchange
The talks we have
There's something there
We both know it
But we don't want to admit it
There's something holding us back
Something we both love too dearly
Maybe in the future
Maybe when we are older.

Laaibah Ahmed (15)

Ali, My Best Friend

Ali is my best friend,
She loves to crochet,
She is the best in every way.
Ali is like me, she is autistic too,
We really have fun when we visit the zoo.
Ali gets me like no one else,
That's why she is my best friend,
In the whole wide world.

Ava Giandiri-Davis (9)

David Walliams

David Walliams is the best author I can find,
This man is very humorous,
The one that inspires me to be a writer.
I, myself, have read all of his books,
My personal favourite is 'The Midnight Gang'.
So thank you, David, for inspiring me,
To be a writer when I'm older.

Jessica Prestage (10)

Nico

N ico loves to run and play

I t's fun and loud when he barks

C areful when you touch him, you don't want to make him hurt

O n every single day, he's kind and always lovable. He isn't just my dog, he's my amazing dog!

Clara Farinella (7)

My Idol, Churchill

You taught,
And this became me,
And even now, I idolise you,
In your greatest power,
And even now, I will remember you,
You destroyed an evil mask,
And now you are beloved across the country,
In our greatest hearts,
God Save the King.

Max Hutton (13)

My Daddy

I admire my daddy,
I love him very much,
His face is itchy to touch.
He is very kind to me,
And always cares for me.
He kisses me to sleep,
But I come down to have a peep!
He always makes delicious food,
Which I eat in a good mood.

Libby Eggertsen (7)

My Friend, My Idol

My idol is my friend,
Our friendship will never end.
Your secrets are untold,
Our love is worth more than gold.
We will be friends forever,
And do everything together.
Everything you say is true,
I am so lucky to have a friend like you.

Inaaya Imtiaz (10)

My Mother

My mother is the best
The most kindest
She taught me how to talk
With her finger, she made me walk
She taught me my deen
And was supportive in my dream
I was a zero
She made me a hero
Her food is the best
Amongst the rest.

Alishba Kauser (12)

Family Comes First

F amily always comes first
A lways be thankful for what you have
M any people are glad that they have a family
I want to let you know how lucky you are
L ive, laugh and love
Y ou are lucky the way you are.

Adaah Afzal (14)

My Dog Best Friend

Dogs may be big, they may be small,
But mine is the best of them all.
My dog is small, but she's bold and crazy.
She's not got thick fur, but she's perfect for all.
She's a Frenchie, small and mighty,
Perfect for anybody.

Shayla-Mai Irwin (11)

My Amazing Mum

M agnificent
Y ogi

A ppreciated
M odest
A dmired
Z oned
I nspirational
N oble
G rateful

M arvellous
U nique
M agical.

Holly Probin (11)

Lovely Mommy

My mom feeds me day and night,
And kisses me goodnight.
When it gets sunny,
It gets funny with my mommy.
When my nose starts running,
My mommy comes running.
I will always love my mommy,
Because her food is always yummy.

Aaron O-King (8)

Lions

Lions are known to be the king of the jungle,
How would you like to meet the carnivore?
It has mighty teeth, strong claws and they are brave,
Lions live in a deep, dark cave.
Lions are phenomenal animals,
Do you agree?

Othniel-Levi Antwi (7)

Tilly

She makes me laugh,
She makes me smile.
She makes me happy,
Laughter = Love.
Love = Kind,
Which means you will never be left behind.
She is she and I am me,
Her name is Tilly, my name is Grace,
We are best friends for ever and ever!

Grace Coggins (9)

The Alley Cats

Dedicated to my cat, Muffin

There were cats in the alley
And in the alley were some cats
The cats in the alley lived by some flats
And fought with the rats in their little tin hats
By the fire, they fought with their little tin hats.

Poppy Teasdill (11)

My Teacher Is The Best!

My teacher is the best!
You may be impressed,
She has beautiful short hair,
And sits in a comfy chair,
She loves creating,
And ice skating,
But sometimes we have to do a test,
But still, she's the *best!*

Emile Krenciute (9)

Sophie

S uper friend to me
O ldest nursery bestie
P roper kind girl
H eart to heart forever
I will always trust you
E xpert at making me... *Happy!*

Sophia Kate Russell (8)

Grandma

You're as bright as the sun
As warm as fire
As colourful as the flowers
As kind as a teddy bear
As beautiful as the horizon
On a deserted island
And I wouldn't have you
Any other way.

Erin Daniels (8)

Kirby

K icking bad guys' butts
I ncredible eating ability
R eally special and round
B eautiful smile and brilliant eyes
Y our pink superhero.

Mia Foster-Murray (5)

My Hero

Nanna was my hero
She loved animals like me
You will always be my hero
1, 2 and 3,
Dance high in the sky
And fly high
Above my eyes.

Princess (La'Lonia-Mai) Cooper (9)

Papidou Pup

Papidou, it's me and you,
Every night when I sleep,
You in my arms I keep,
My best pup,
Until the sun comes up,
I wake up to cuddle you,
Papi-doodle do!

Benjamin West (6)

Firefighters

Firefighters are the fastest in town
Superheroes, the best around
Saving animals and people
They spray the water
And stop the fire.

Matias Cristea (6)

My Mum...

My mum
She is a beautiful queen.
And she's inspired me to follow my dream.
I love her so
And I want her to know.
That she will always be my hero.

Amirah Osman (10)

My Cat, Nacho

He is fluffy
And ginger
And he pounces
Like a ninja
He likes playing
And fighting
And also
Likes biting.

Sophie Carberry (7)

Summer Songs

We came like the waves,
Just like a hundred songs saved,
Together, we can climb the sky,
Together, we will let the summer day roll by.

Sasha Green (15)

Kilo

My favourite pet is my dog, Kilo,
He is so lovely,
He listens to me carefully,
And he is super cute.

Freya-Lilly Burrows (5)

Young Writers Information

We hope you have enjoyed reading this book – and that you will continue to in the coming years.

If you're the parent or family member of an enthusiastic poet or story writer, do visit our website **www.youngwriters.co.uk/subscribe** and sign up to receive news, competitions, writing challenges and tips, activities and much, much more! There's lots to keep budding writers motivated!

If you would like to order further copies of this book, or any of our other titles, then please give us a call or order via your online account.

Young Writers
Remus House
Coltsfoot Drive
Peterborough
PE2 9BF
(01733) 890066
info@youngwriters.co.uk

Join in the conversation!
Tips, news, giveaways and much more!

 YoungWritersUK  YoungWritersCW  youngwriterscw